THE WELL ADJUSTED CAT

"You take your dog to the vet, and expect him to feel better fast. But if your pet's back is hurting or spine needs adjusting, you're out of luck—most states do not allow chiropractors to work on animals, and only a handful of veterinarians know anything about chiropractic, says Dr. Daniel Kamen, expert on treating anything from sedated lions to llamas. He'll tell you why pet owners should adjust their own dogs' backs, and how to do it."   —*Radio & TV Report* (1996)

"Sorry, he won't do giraffes anymore—but if your dog, cat or horse has a back out of whack, Dr. Daniel Kamen is your man."
                                                    —*Star* (1987)

"An Illinois chiropractor is using his skills on animals, and he says the technique works as well on dogs, cats, and horses as it does on humans. An added benefit, says Dr. Daniel R. Kamen of Buffalo Grove, is that four-legged patients don't talk back."
                                                    —*Insight* (1986)

"Kamen is a chiropractor with a twist. His main occupation is treating people with back or arthritic problems. However, his sideline is treating animals. He has treated a giraffe, a lion, a bear, a monkey, and several cats, horses and dogs... 'Admittedly, there isn't a big calling for lion chiropractors,' said Kamen. 'You just don't find that many lions or bears in the suburbs.'"
                                    —*Countryside ReminderNews* (1984)

"Though he wants to steer clear of legal beagles, Kamen argued, 'We have evidence that chiropractic works on humans. Animals have similar nervous systems and spines, so I believe chiropractic would help them too.'" —*Chicago Sun-Times* (1982)

The

Well Adjusted Cat

Feline Chiropractic Methods You Can Do

by Dr. Daniel R. Kamen, D.C.

BROOK
L I N E
BOOKS

Illustrations ©1997 by Amy Sibiga.
Cover art and design by Roger Gordy.
Interior design and typography by Erica L. Schultz.

Disclaimer (to cat owners or anyone else who reads this book): This book is about managing vertebral subluxations in cats, not treating disease. Do not use this book in place of veterinary care. All health questions concerning your cat, including those pertaining to the use of chiropractic care, must initially be addressed by your veterinarian.

The author and anyone or anything associated with the writing, production, or distribution of this book assumes **ABSOLUTELY NO** liability to or for anyone (man or beast) who uses the information presented in this book. The reader or user of the information presented in this book assumes the entire responsibility and liability for his or her actions.

International Standard Book Number: 1-57129-044-3
Library of Congress Catalog Card Number: 97-75000

Printed in Canada by Best Book Manufacturers, Louiseville, Quebec.
10 9 8 7 6 5 4 3 2 1

Published by
BROOKLINE BOOKS
P.O. Box 1047 • Cambridge, MA 02238-1047
Order toll-free: 1-800-666-BOOK

Contents

FOR TINKERBELL AND BUBBLES
MY LONG GONE BUT NOT FORGOTTEN CATS

* * *

My inspiration to write this book came from several sources. I would like to mention a few of them.

My lovely and brilliant wife, Sharon, and Ruth and Victor Kaufman (parents of the bride).

My parents, Jack (Pop) and Shirley (Bubby Meow) Kamen.

My sisters, Joyce and Suzy, and my brother David.

My three talented sons, Jeffrey, Gary, and Kevin.

To Amy Sibiga—great artwork, again.

To the two most knowledgeable computer people I've ever known: Steve Loring, who created my web page (check it out at http://www.miint.net/~kamen/), and Ken Kirby.

To Dr. Ron Neuerburg, D.C.

To Dr. Greg Linn.

To Sadi Ranson and Milton Budoff at Brookline Books. Thanks again.

PREFACE

Why chiropractic? What does chiropractic offer the animal kingdom that allopathic medicine doesn't?

These questions, along with many others, will be answered in *The Well Adjusted Cat*. But in brief, the classic response from most chiropractors is that chiropractic gets to the *cause* of the condition. This is not to say the cause of all diseases can be rooted out through chiropractic care. But many can. Pain relievers cover up the symptoms of an illness. Aspirin merely shuts off the alarm while the fire still rages. Chiropractors direct much of their attention at the spine, which is the "fuse box" of the body. This is often the place where dis-ease begins. Luckily, nature made the spinal columns of both man and beast accessible enough to be manipulated by hand without being invasive, thus making chiropractic therapy available to one and all.

The fact that animal chiropractic has yet to become mainstream has nothing to do with the art, science, and efficacy of chiropractic as a healing system. Rather, the question of *who should administer the procedures* has been the bane of its perpetuation. Most chiropractors licensed in the United States are forbidden by law to practice their art on animals, and veterinarians are too busy with the numerous everyday emergencies to give chiropractic a second glance. So what's the solution?

Offering a pet owner's guide to feline chiropractic methods

does not adequately address this question. Nothing can take the place of professional chiropractic care. But until chiropractic and veterinary schools teach these methods at the front door of their institutions, the delivery of animal chiropractic care is up for grabs. In the meantime, it is the responsibility of the pet owner to make an informed decision. However, any decision you as the pet owner make should be made in tandem with a holistic veterinarian.

It is my hope that you will be entertained as well as educated by the following pages. Just remember the words of my great-grandfather Otis Rutherford Kamen, "If it ain't broken, it don't belong to me!"

—*Daniel R. Kamen, B.A., D.C.*

Introduction

CATaclysm

The chances of me writing a book about Feline Chiropractic Methods You Can Do without interjecting a little sarcasm are about the same as the chances of John Wayne ordering the bartender to bring him a Fuzzy Navel. Although the well-being of cats is the essence of this book, I feel it would be of great interest (and possibly amusement) to the reader to know what has happened to me since the publishing of my first "how-to" animal chiropractic book, *The Well Adjusted Dog,* which made its way into the hands of dog owners in August, 1996.

When my book hit the stores, the response was mixed. Dog owners loved it, even though some of them were reluctant to administer the methods themselves. Veterinarians didn't know what to make of it (actually, some of them did, but let them write their own book). Chiropractors, while glad to know there's another market for their services, kept asking me why I would want non-professionals to adjust their own pets. But then, most who asked this question stopped and thought, "Oh, yeah. I, as a licensed chiropractor, am not allowed to adjust animals. I forgot." But I didn't forget!

As the author of these "how-to" animal adjusting books, I must accept the responsibility for this. After all, I don't have to teach dog or cat owners how to adjust their pets. But I know chiropractic makes animals healthier, and an at-home safe adjustment is much better than none at all.

The media really enjoys this confusion about animal chiropractic. And why? Because animal chiropractic is still very controversial. As of this writing, there are still no states that allow the autonomous practice of animal chiropractic by a licensed chiropractor. In some states, its practice by a chiropractor is allowed in the presence of a veterinarian.

If a chiropractor treats an animal other than a Chia Pet, he or she is in for some ridicule, as exemplified by the following exchange I had with a veterinarian who called in during an interview with a Los Angeles radio show.

"We're back with Dr. Kamen, an animal chiropractor and author of the book, *The Well Adjusted Dog: Canine Chiropractic Methods You Can Do*," the host, Bob Valley, said. "And we have a caller. Dr. I.M. Thor [not his real name], a local veterinarian. You're on the air, Dr. Thor."

"Thank you," Dr. Thor said. "I just want to caution your listeners about trying chiropractic for your dog. If it is as great as Dr. Kamen says it is, then why don't veterinary schools teach it as part of their core curriculum? I went to one of the nation's finest vet colleges (University of Illinois) and they never made mention of chiropractic there. It has not been proven."

Even after all the well-documented clinical studies that have been published which validate chiropractic, I was somewhat surprised to hear a well-educated individual make such an uninformed remark. Just to appease my own curiosity, I just had to ask him a different question. "Do you think animal psychiatry is worthwhile? Do they embrace it in vet school?"

"Yes, of course. It is a valuable behavioral science and specialty which helps the pet to function in its intended environment," Dr. Thor said.

"Like what?" I asked.

"Well, several things," the vet continued. "Interacting with people, interacting with other animals, and sexual dysfunction are just a few reasons why pet psychiatry is necessary. But one of the most common benefits of pet psychiatry is when a dog changes homes or owners. This confuses them, since dogs are essentially wolves who are used to one leader of the pack. It's very difficult for a dog to change its allegiance from one owner to another."

"Those are all valid reasons," I said. "Since I know very little about pet psychiatry, I'm in no position to argue with you. But you mentioned something about sexual dysfunction. Is this really a problem among pets? Do they have some sort of performance anxiety?"

Mr. Valley didn't know where I was going with this one. (I wasn't sure where I was going either.) Mr. Valley quickly interrupted. "Doctors," he said, "you're straying from the subject at hand, animal chiropractic."

"No, no," Dr. Thor said. "I'll answer Dr. Kamen's question. Yes, animals can have performance anxiety, especially when the owners expect the dogs to perform at a specific place and time. We're usually talking about high-strung and expensive purebreds that are bred for profit. Timing is very important."

"I see. But this sounds more like owner anxiety. What does the psychiatrist say to the dog to help him?"

"The therapy is usually a series of exercises along with vocal intonations and recording the various responses."

"Does the dog lay on a couch?" I asked.

"No," Dr. Thor said.

"Under the couch?" asked Mr. Valley.

"Do they show the dog folded ink blots of naked bats?" I interrupted.

"This is getting silly," the vet said.

"Not so silly," I added. "I once had a dog come to me for sexual dysfunction. I was able to diagnose the cause in a matter of seconds. All I did was ask the dog what he thought was causing his trouble. Do you know what he said? 'Every time (woof, woof) I got in the mood (woof, woof, woof), someone would whack my nose with a newspaper (ruff). If that isn't enough, at three weeks old they cut my pee-pee, I hated my sire and my mother was a bitch.'"

Mr. Valley let out a laugh, and I think his sound engineer giggled a little too. That's the problem with radio, you can't judge the immediate response of your entire audience. But I was secretly wishing they had deleted my last remark.

"That's ridiculous," Dr. Thor said. "I can't believe that a professional such as yourself would make light of such a serious subject, especially since you're teaching others about their pet's health."

"That's another thing," said Mr. Valley. "Did you know that Dr. Kamen is holding an animal chiropractic seminar next month in Los Angeles? He teaches veterinarians and chiropractors to adjust all types of animals including dogs, cats, and even horses."

"Yes I did," said Dr. Thor, chuckling as if to shake his head in smug disgust. "I got one of his postcards advertising his seminar. I, for one, will not be attending.

"Any particular reason?" asked Mr. Valley.

"Yes, many. For one, he teaches this to chiropractors. In California, a chiropractor cannot practice on animals. Thus, Dr. Kamen is encouraging chiropractors to break the law. I will not be a part of it."

Dr. Thor was only partially right. It just so happens that California is one of those states where a chiropractor *can* practice on animals under a veterinarian's supervision. I always inform the seminar registrants that the laws governing the practice of animal chiropractic differ from state to state. I try to research and report this information as accurately as possible.

"Not only that," Dr. Thor continued, "but I contacted the veterinary board here and made them aware of Dr. Kamen's impending seminar."

The timing of Dr. Thor's last statement couldn't have been better. No sooner had he finished his last statement than Mr. Valley introduced his next caller. "We have Dr. Will Spayer [not his real name] on the line," said Mr. Valley. "He's a member of California's veterinary board. You have a comment for Dr. Kamen?"

"Yes," said Dr. Spayer. "I know about Dr. Kamen's seminars. I've heard some very good things about them. Positive things. But I've got to tell you, Dr. Kamen, I'm not happy."

"You're not what?" I asked.

"Happy. I'm not happy."

"Dr. Spayer, do you know who I am?"

"Yes, you're Dr. Kamen. You call yourself an animal chiropractor."

"That's right," I said. "Chiropractor. I'm a chiropractor, not a psychiatrist. If you're not happy, you have to call a psychiatrist. I'm afraid I can't help you. That would be practicing a discipline which is *way* out of my field."

"That's funny," Mr. Valley chortled. "We were just talking about psychiatrists."

I heard the sound of receivers clicking. Both vets had hung up.

I never wanted to be a veterinarian. My first choice as a serious vocation was chiropractic. Once I discovered chiropractic, I never looked back. My interest in animal chiropractic started when I was in my second year of chiropractic school. One of the professors who taught anatomy, Dr. Gilbert Schmiedel [his real name], used to adjust animals in his office at the Palmer College of Chiropractic in Davenport, Iowa. I can remember one afternoon I was walking down the hall and heard a yelp coming from one of the rooms. It didn't sound human. I knocked on the door and another student opened it for me. Dr. Schmiedel invited me to observe a canine adjustment. At that moment I thought to myself, "Why not?" Here was a large, virtually untapped source of new patients who could really benefit from chiropractic care. I was awestruck as I watched Dr. Schmiedel twist the dog's head one way, then the other, then turn the dog on its back to adjust the lumbars (lower spine).

"Can you show me a few moves?" I asked Dr. Schmiedel.

I no longer had him as a teacher, since I had already passed his course the previous semester. I therefore felt we were on the same level, colleagues of sorts, and presumed I could ask this of him.

"Sure," he said. "Come back tomorrow around this time. I have a lady bringing in three cats and a dog."

I couldn't believe my luck. I was going to have a private tutoring session with the master of all masters of animal chiropractic. So I made sure I was there on time. When I arrived, there were five other students who also wanted to see the genius at work.

The first case was a male cat who couldn't stop shaking his head. The young woman who brought him in told the doc that this cat had a habit of crawling up into her basement ceiling, between the roof and the tiles, then finding an opening at the end of the ceiling, where he would jump down onto the couch below. Only this time, she was sleeping on the couch, and the cat jumped on her head. This startled her so badly that she screamed and flung the cat across the room with her arm, causing the injury. The cat wasn't in constant pain, but he just couldn't get comfortable. Something was pinching him. Nothing on the cat was broken, as verified by X-rays which had been taken by a vet the day after the incident. Dr. Schmiedel grabbed the cat with one hand (he had BIG hands) and with the other, grasped the cat's head, which made the tiny head disappear altogether. He then tucked the cat's head down and gave it a quick twist to the right. One of the students let out a loud "whoa," but the cat didn't mind. Instead the newly adjusted feline walked along the floor, *without* shaking his head. I was hooked! From that point on, I made it my business to learn everything I could about animal chiropractic.

Now, fifteen years after graduation, I'm still learning more about animal chiropractic, and I'm also surprised. I'm surprised that animal chiropractic isn't practiced as widely as it should be. It's the fault of those arcane laws that tie the hands of chiropractors. The absurdities of these laws were highlighted by an article written by well-known syndicated columnist Mike Royko, of the *Chicago Tribune* (see Appendix B).

On Tuesday, October 29th, 1996, I woke up at precisely 6:00 a.m., the time my wife, Sharon, sets the radio alarm. I had spoken to Mr. Royko two days earlier about my plight with animal chiropractic and the laws that bind my hands. I told Sharon that I felt the Royko article would appear today, and that it was sitting out there by itself on our driveway. I had to rescue it! So, in my haste to get the paper (and we've all been there), I put on the pair of dress pants sitting on the floor from the night before, a Three Stooges T-shirt, a pair of untied Nikes, and a bathrobe. I flew out of the house to retrieve the goods. My next door neighbor, Clark, was walking his dog and saw me scurry out of the house.

"Relaxed the ol' dress code for work, eh?" Clark asked.

"Naw, I have to see if Royko made mincemeat out of me or the politicians."

Clark reached for his own paper to see for himself. I told him to watch out for the article. And sure enough, there it was. "Animal Chiropractor Has a Bone to Pick with State Agency," the heading read. It was a glorious piece, right on page three, Mr. Royko's usual spot. He gave it to the lawmakers, but good. He explained that I can legally buy a hunting license and shoot a deer's head off, but I'm not allow to adjust its spine. Now *that's* ironic.

By coincidence, I met Clark outside again on my way to

work. He liked the article, and told me to expect the unexpected that day. He was right.

Aside from getting calls from other newspapers (*The Examiner*), radio shows, and TV shows (*EXTRA*), I got a call from a guy who introduced himself as Dr. Floyd Gimble, a chiropractor from Kankakee, Illinois, not terribly far from my city. Dr. Gimble was very excited about the article and thought it shed chiropractic in a very positive light. He had me on the phone for about twenty minutes, asking me if I'd heard from vets or any group who wanted to wring my neck. I answered each of his questions with as much humor and enthusiasm I could.

There was one question Dr. Gimble asked me that I particularly went to town with. He wanted to know what would be the difference between the veterinary and the chiropractic approaches to conducting a spinal examination on an animal. Since I was in one of my more jocular moods, I told him, "Well, for starters, a chiropractor has a lot fewer diagnostic tools to use than a vet. A chiropractor can use his eyes to observe his patient in motion; with his ears, hear his patient indicate pain; and with his hands, feel the joints of his patient's body."

I've got to tell you, I had some fun with this conversation. I was laughing, Dr. Gimble was laughing, and a mysterious voice in the background was laughing. But I didn't know who this mysterious voice belonged to—until later that night.

About 9:30 p.m., I was going over my voice-mail messages. My pager was going crazy. There were a dozen calls from people around the Chicago area, calling to tell me they had *just heard me on the radio*.

"What?" I screeched. "I didn't do an interview just now. What are you talking about?"

It turns out that my new pal, Dr. Gimble, was not good old Doc Gimble at all. He was a DJ from a local radio station, and he ambushed me! But I wasn't angry. Two reasons. First, it was my fault for being so unassuming, and two, he mentioned my book, which was sure to help sales. I have learned that what they say is true. It doesn't matter what is said about you on the air, so long as they spell (or say) your name correctly.

A few weeks later, I got a call from a nationally syndicated TV show, NBC's *EXTRA!*. They wanted to do a segment on animal chiropractic. Right from my office! How could I say no?

The next week, the whole crew came through my door. I had some of my human patients bring in their pets to be filmed for the show. We had three dogs, including an adorable miniature dachshund, a rabbit, and a guinea pig (mine).

Incidentally, as of this writing, I don't have a dog. I used to. My family had three dogs over a thirty-year period. But since I travel so much, and my son is allergic to dogs, we decided not to get one. But a radio show host once asked me towards the end of an interview what kind of dog I had. I had to tell him the truth. He said, "Do you mean to tell me you don't have a dog, and you call yourself an expert on canine chiropractic?" I told him, "That's right. But you can make that same argument for a male gynecologist!" He cut to a commercial.

My biggest fear of appearing on *EXTRA!* was not the camera. It was having the Illinois Department of Professional Regulation busting in during the taping and seeing animals being adjusted in my office. You see, at about the same time, they were investigating me, and I had told them truthfully that I wasn't adjusting animals in my office. But happily, the investigators never showed up the day of the shooting and it was safe to do the show.

EXTRA! taped for about two hours in my office. We later went to a stable to demonstrate how horses were adjusted. The show was aired four weeks after the shoot. My patients were thrilled to see their pets on TV. I got lots of calls and exposure for animal chiropractic. But not a peep out of the state! Were they getting soft, or trying to avoid a confrontation with me and the good people of Illinois who want chiropractic care for their pets?

The world may never know the answer to that question. All I know is that chiropractic is over a hundred years old and there's still no clear-cut answer to who should be the ones adjusting animals. Until this question is answered, or until state laws allow chiropractors to freely practice on animals, I hope this book will at least give cat owners some insight on how chiropractic can be applied to their pets, safely and at home.

CHAPTER 1

THE OUTLAW DOC
(THE NOT~SO~QUIET
WYATT EARP)

First of all, if any member of any state veterinary board visits my office to complain about my animal chiropractic seminars, I don't want them showing up in a $40,000 chinchilla coat. I'm not a member of PETA (People for the Ethical Treatment of Animals), and I have nothing against people eating meat (I don't), or wearing leather coats (I do). But who are these naysayers who speak out against animal chiropractic, yet see nothing wrong with clipping ears, bobbing tails, and declawing cats? All in the name of humanity? Or all in the name of money! We're all part of the same hypocrisy.

When I set out to make animal chiropractic an honorable profession (circa 1981), I was unaware that most state veterinary boards (and even some chiropractic boards) safeguarded themselves from this happening. The language used to describe the scope of practice in the Minnesota Chiropractic Practice Act, for example, reads "the science of adjusting any abnormal articulations of the *human* body" (italics mine). I'm not sure who oversaw the drafting of this particular statue, but it seems to me that someone (possibly a vet) had the vision and political pull to add "human" to the law. From where I'm sitting, this is definitely a "keep off the grass" sign.

I found that even my own backyard is off limits. I live in the northwest suburbs of Chicago. A dozen and a half miles to the west is The National College Of Chiropractic, the third largest chiropractic school in the world (next to Life College in Marietta, GA, and Palmer University in Davenport, IA). Since National is so close and has a sizable student population, I thought it would be a good idea to start there. I wrote them a letter asking permission to rent a classroom on their campus to conduct an animal chiropractic seminar. They sent me a response stating that the term "animal chiropractic" was "*a misnomer. The application of manipulative techniques to animals may constitute a form of veterinary procedure but does not constitute 'chiropractic' procedure. It is, therefore, not sanctioned nor taught at this college. Accordingly, Dr. Kamen, your request is respectfully denied.*"

I respect National College's right to rent space to whomever they wish. I also think that National is a very fine institution and, most importantly, graduates high-caliber chiropractors. But I wish they, being the progressive school they are, could see what I see: a bleak view for chiropractors due to the recent economic climate—namely, managed care.

Animal chiropractors do not take away business from veterinarians. When animals needs drugs or surgery, they go to a vet. Likewise, when animals need subluxations removed, they should be taken to a chiropractor or someone trained in animal chiropractic. When was the last time a competent chiropractor dissuaded a heart patient from having heart surgery?

During the last couple of years of being on the road, and teaching animal chiropractic methods to professionals, I've discovered an amazing, almost awe-inspiring phenomenon. In states like California, where chiropractors are allowed to work with vets and adjust animals, *both practices reaped huge benefits*. The chiropractor usually maintained his or her human practice and worked at the vet's office once or twice a week. And both professionals discovered something: Veterinarians have animal patients who are owned by people, and chiropractors have people patients who own animals. The marriage of these two professions is the greatest, no-cost, cross-referral engine there is in health care! "I looked in the mirror and the enemy is me."

For those who might think that animal chiropractic has opposition from vets the same way human chiropractic had opposition from the American Medical Association, you're wrong! There is no conspiracy from the American Veterinary Medical Association (AVMA: the veterinary AMA) to contain and destroy chiropractic. Why? Because the AVMA doesn't have that kind of muscle. Human medical doctors who wish to work at certain hospitals and be paid by certain third party payers, must play the "good old boys" game. Don't make waves, and don't stray from the beaten path, or "there's the door." Vets are much more independent. They own their hospitals, and they don't have to prove themselves to HMO's or other health insurance companies, since they run essentially all-cash practices. This makes vets more ethical than the average doctor (chiropractors included), since they collect a fair-market fee for a fair-market service. Vets are also independent thinkers and should be commended for that. There are several veterinarian-based alternative health care associations, including the International Veterinary Acupuncture Society (IVAS), the American Holistic Veterinary Medical Association, and the California Holistic Veterinary Medical Association (see Appendix C).

With additional training, coupled with public demand, there should be a place in this country for existing and future chiropractors to treat animals. Our four-legged friends and their owners deserve chiropractic care. It is up to you and me to see that they get it.

CHAPTER 2

THE SUBLUXATION

Chiropractic Definition of a Vertebral Subluxation: The physiological and neurological disturbances caused by two adjacent vertebrae pinching a spinal nerve and its related structures. In other words, a vertebra misaligned on top of another vertebra will cause pinching of the spinal nerve in between.

A vertebral subluxation reflects the body's desperate need to respond and adapt to adverse mechanical, chemical, or mental stimuli. The organ victimized by these stimuli—let's say the stomach—will try to send an emergency SOS via the spinal cord to the brain. However, this neurological signal will be blunted by tight spinal muscles gripping and choking the vertebrae that house the spinal nerve belonging to the stomach, thus impairing the "cable" and robbing the stomach of neurological impulses. This, in turn, requires other organs to "make up the slack," thereby creating a tremendous strain on the entire system.

ARE SUBLUXATIONS PAINFUL?

This is probably the most important question anyone could ask about chiropractic. But the initial answer to this question is a non-committal one: sometimes. The subluxation does not always hurt. In fact, they are mostly "silent." When people visit a chiropractor, they don't come in because they think they're subluxated, they come in because they're in pain. By the time someone has pain, the subluxation complex is deeply rooted in the body.

There are seven phases to the vertebral subluxation: *misalignment*, *neuropathy*, *kinesiopathy*, *dysfunction*, *symptoms*, *degeneration*, and *compensation*. **Note:** Sometimes all the phases can occur within a short period of time (a day or less), and sometimes the subluxation can fester for weeks or months before the patient comes in with pain or dysfunction.

1. **Misalignment** is the first phase of a subluxation and is usually caused by trauma. If your cat chases a squirrel up a tree, then falls, his muscles will splint the traumatized area to prevent further injury. This will alter the way he walks and might even cause disc pressure.

2. **Neuropathy** is the second phase. This is when the Intervertebral Foramen (IVF) becomes compromised. With the IVF closed by the misalignment, the spinal nerve becomes compressed and less vital.

3. **Kinesiopathy** is the third phase. This is deranged joint motion where the area becomes stiff or fixed. A lot of physiological changes take place here, including joint swelling, scarring, adhesion formation, *vascular* (blood vessel) stress, and muscle atrophy. It is also possible for kinesiopathy to denote excess joint motion (*hypermobility*). If the initial trauma caused tissue damage (such as a tear), the ligaments may become weak and loose.

4. **Dysfunction** is when the joints and tissues (muscles) don't perform as they should. Limping, head bobbing, and an abnormal gait are signs of dysfunction.

5. **Symptoms** are what bring the patient in the door. *Pain* is the operative word here. Predictably, by the time you see the patient in pain, the subluxation process is already four phases deep and is now part of the body. This is why you have to catch the subluxations in the early stages. Prevention is key.

6. **Degeneration** is one step past pain. Disease and tissue destruction ensues. By this time the patient needs your help whether he wants it or not. It is at this phase that a nonbeliever in chiropractic becomes an evangelist after the treatment.

7. **Compensations** are often mistaken for subluxations since they share similar characteristics such as muscle spasms and restricted motion. An example of a compensation is when you subluxate your lower back and then have to twist your upper back while you walk (to lessen the pain). Your upper back is the area that compensates for your lower back pain. The property of a subluxation that's generally missing from a compensation is heat. A true spinal subluxation will feel warm, because heat denotes inflammation, which is one of the signs of a pinched spinal nerve.

Primary Causes of Feline Subluxations

The two leading causes of feline subluxations are injuries and poisons. But cats, because of their amazing flexibility, suffer considerably fewer injury-related subluxations than dogs. It is poisons, especially those ingested in food, that are responsible for the majority of feline distress.

How Poisons Cause Subluxations

To understand how poisons or other toxins can cause that "kink" in your spine called the subluxation, I'd like to refer back to a quote by Dr. Daniel David Palmer, the founder of chiropractic. Dr. Palmer wrote about the "one question [that] was always uppermost in my mind in my search for the cause of disease. I desired to know why one person was ailing and why his associate, eating at the same table, working in the same shop, at the same bench, was not." The point here is that everyone is born with strengths and weaknesses. If you are genetically programmed to get sick at an early age, you will. This is true most of the time. Of course, eating right and exercising can make a difference. And a well-timed open-heart bypass operation can add years to your life. But for the most part, we're doomed. The best you can do is take control of the things you can, and don't worry about the rest.

How does this relate to your cat?

Most cat owners are well-meaning individuals who love animals. The only thing they might be guilty of is being uninformed. For example, the majority of cat owners are not aware just how contaminated most store-bought cat food is. Since the main ingredient in cat food is meat, the toxins start with how the food animal was raised. Cows, for example, are fed grain which is usually treated with pesticides and other chemicals. Then the cow is usually given steroids so she'll grow bigger and faster. Once the cow is slaughtered, the meat is often prepared with chemical preservatives such as *ethoxyquin*. This preservative is frequently found in expensive dog and cat foods, which people buy because they think it's better for their pet. Actually, ethoxyquin was developed by Monsanto as a rubber hardener and insecticide, and is known to cause kidney and liver failure, as well as cancer and thyroid conditions (*The Natural Remedy Book for Dogs and Cats*, p. 17).

If a toxic chemical known to cause liver disease is eaten by a cat, then those spinal nerves which control the liver will become stressed and subluxated. Now the cat has a major organ, the liver, that isn't functioning properly. So what happens now? The rest of the body has to make up the slack. Here's an example of a six-cylinder engine pulling the eight-cylinder cat!

Food is only one of many sources where a cat can ingest toxins. Household products such as rat poisons, mouse baits, and ant traps contain harmful chemicals such as arsenic, sodium fluoracetate, and metaldehyde. Both cats and dogs are attracted to antifreeze because it tastes sweet to them. Antifreeze can be fatal if ingested in small amounts. Petroleum products, if inhaled, can cause severe lung conditions such as pneumonia, and thus cause subluxations to the spinal nerves relating to the lungs.

So what's a cat owner to do? How can you protect your cat

from consuming all of this garbage? You must learn how to feed and take better care of your cat. The book I highly recommend for this is called *The Natural Remedy Book For Dogs & Cats*, by Diane Stein (Crossing Press, 1994). This will give you all the information you'll need to start your cat on a healthy lifestyle. In the meantime, find and remove as many vertebral subluxations you can, and get rid of those ant traps!

OTHER CAUSES OF FELINE SUBLUXATIONS

1. **Improper bedding.** Cats should be comfortable. Their flexible bodies can adapt to several types of bedding such as the soft bean-bag variety (polystyrene beads), a blanket in a cardboard box, or your plush carpeted floor. If you buy a bed for your cat, make sure the bed gives him enough room to move around. Cramped quarters will limit his body movement and cause subluxations.

2. **Caged cats.** If there is no room to move around, there is no way to relieve muscular stress. "Confinement will cause misalignment" is a good motto to remember. This is also true if a cat is injured. Confinement is helpful for the more serious injuries, but people tend to over-rest their cats after an injury. Muscles get weak and start to atrophy in just a few days. To retain healthy muscle tone, a cat should be free to walk around whenever possible. Exercise is very important. Your cat can't stay healthy without it. If you live in a high-rise, you should provide exercise equipment for your cat such as

a scratching post. Kittens should be taught to play with safe toys, such as a firm cloth-covered ball, which encourages life-long activity. (According to Dr. David Taylor, a leading British veterinarian, three breeds of cats are not suited for indoor living: the Somali, the Abyssinian, and the Rex.)

3. **Fleas.** Your cat will contort his body to scratch the itches, thus causing subluxations. Over-the-counter flea treatments work well, but they often contain chemicals such as methoprene and permethrin that can be toxic to the owner as well as the pet. Control fleas naturally by adding a few teaspoons of apple cider vinegar in the water bowl each day. According to Diane Stein, "[this] makes the pet's blood inhospitable to fleas." Ms. Stein's other flea control advice: "Make a spray of a teaspoon of three percent food-grade hydrogen peroxide and two ounces of aloe vera juice, and spray on the pet. This helps to repel fleas, plus eases flea-allergy dermatitis."

4. **Obesity.** This is by far a more serious problem with dogs. You just don't see too many fat cats (unless you visit City Hall). Anyway, the average cat should weigh close to 12 pounds (depending on breed). The cat's weight is something the owner can completely control.

5. **Having too much fun.** I'm not referring to the cat's fun. This is in reference to the owner's children. Kids sometimes like to test the limits of their cat's righting reflex. This is where they turn the cat upside down,

drop him from a few feet up, and watch him land on his feet. *Never do this.* Cats use their righting reflex to save their lives. A cat might land on his feet when dropped from ten feet, but he'll seriously hurt himself.

6. **Stress.** This usually stems from living in an unsafe environment, or one in which the animal feels threatened (often by other animals in the household).

CHAPTER 3

THE PHYSICAL FELINE

Before you get crackin', you'll need to know a few of the basics about cat anatomy, particularly the musculoskeletal system. *Musculoskeletal* is a compound word encompassing body parts belonging to the skeleton (bones), muscles, joints and related soft tissues such as ligaments, tendons and nerves. A *ligament* is a tough fibrous tissue which holds two or more bones together, thus forming a joint. A *tendon* is inelastic fibrous tissue that connects a muscle to a bone. For example, your Achilles tendon (the thickest and strongest tendon in the body) connects with your calf (lower leg) muscles and anchors them into the heel of your foot (Fig. 3-1). *Nerves* are tissues that detect sensation and motion, energize muscles and organs, and convey impulses between the brain or spinal cord and all the other parts of the body.

While studying the structure of the cat, pay close attention to how the bones relate to each other, namely as joints. Remember, chiropractic is not about setting bones or fractures. Orthopedic surgeons do that. What chiropractic *is* about is restoring normal joint function wherever possible, with your eye on removing vertebral subluxations in particular. A joint not riddled with arthritis or disease still has a chance to return to normal. Also keep in mind that by restoring normal joint

Achilles tendon

Fig. 3-1.
(Back view of human
right leg.) The
Achilles tendon
anchors the calf
muscles to the heel.

function, you are helping to restore normal soft tissue function, mainly nerves, muscles and ligaments. Functionally sound soft tissues are the integral components of good health.

You should read this section with your cat in your lap. The diagrams only give you a two-dimensional perspective of your cat, while holding your cat on your lap gives you fleas.

Think of your cat's bones as a series of levers. The long bones of the front and back limbs are easy to grasp and manipulate. The smaller, irregular bones of the spine are at times more difficult to maneuver, requiring more patience and skill during the examination and adjusting procedures. Try to feel each area of your cat (except the very sensitive places) as explained in this chapter.

CAT BONES

The cat body is composed of about 244 bones, with certain variations. The number of tail (*caudal*) bones vary from a minimum of 0 to 3 as in the "tail-less" Manx cat, to 28 tail bones in other breeds. The number of toes, too, sometimes varies between breeds.

THE SPINAL COLUMN (VERTEBRAE)

The cat spine is divided into three areas: the *cervical* region (seven neck vertebrae), the *thoracic* region (thirteen mid-back vertebrae), and the *lumbar* region (seven lower-back vertebrae).

Cervicals (Neck Bones)

All mammals, including cats, have seven neck bones (cervicals). The only two exceptions are the manatee (sea cow) and the three-toed sloth, who have six. People are often amazed to learn that a mouse has as many neck bones as a giraffe. Even whales have seven cervicals, but they are fused together; therefore, the whale cannot rotate his head without moving his whole body, much like a person suffering from whiplash.

The first neck bone is called the *atlas* (Fig. 3-2). It is located directly beneath the base of the skull. The atlas looks like no other vertebra. It has a ring-like shape, with two large wings which can readily be felt at both sides of the base of the skull (Fig. 3-3). By feeling these spots on your cat, you can determine if your cat is subluxated and what type of adjustment is needed (see Chapter 7). The joint formed between the base of the skull (*occiput*) and the atlas allows your cat to move his head up (*extension*) and down (*flexion*) and is therefore referred to as the "yes" joint.

The word *atlas* is akin to the word for a bound collection of world maps. The atlas vertebra acts as a pedestal that supports

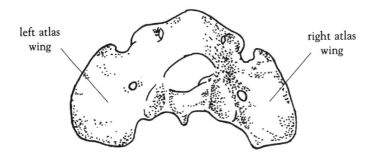

left atlas wing

right atlas wing

Fig. 3-2.
(As viewed while sitting behind your cat.) The first neck bone is the *atlas*. It is a ring-like bone which is felt under the base of the skull.

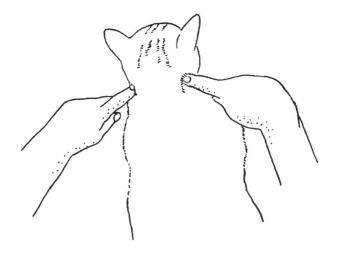

Fig. 3-3.
The atlas wings can be felt at both sides of the base of the skull.

the globe or head. The bone directly underneath the atlas is called the *axis*, or second cervical (Fig. 3-4). There is a projection emanating from the axis called the *dens*. The dens fits into the ring of the atlas and acts as a rotational point for the head, much like the world revolves around its axis. Since the joint formed by the atlas and the axis allows the neck to rotate, it is commonly referred to as the "No" joint. This universal anatomical phenomenon exemplifies how all the world's creatures are related on some level.

The axis, as well as all the other cervical vertebrae, has something the atlas doesn't have—a *spinous process* (Fig. 3-5). These "spinouses," or "spines" as they are commonly called, are the prominences or "bumps" you feel as you run your fingers down your cat's back. The spines are used as adjusting contact

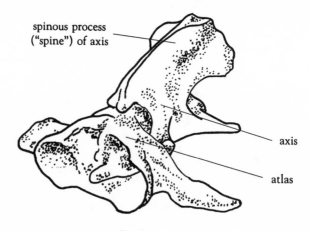

spinous process
("spine") of axis

axis

atlas

Fig. 3-4.
The *axis*, or second cervical (neck bone), is located directly behind (*caudal* to) the atlas.

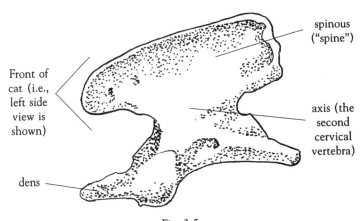

Front of cat (i.e., left side view is shown)

dens

spinous ("spine")

axis (the second cervical vertebra)

Fig. 3-5.
The axis, or second neck bone, has a flat, blade-like "spine" known as the *spinous process*.

points. Being familiar with them and how they feel is essential to performing the chiropractic methods.

All of the cervical vertebrae except the atlas have spines; however, most of the cervical spines *cannot* be felt. This is because the spines belonging to the third through sixth cervicals are short and situated deep within the musculature. The spines of these vertebrae can only be felt in an emaciated animal. Additionally, the inward or *lordotic* curve of the neck makes palpating these spines even more difficult. The only other cervical "spine" that can readily be felt is the seventh cervical. The seventh cervical has a long spine and feels more like a vertebra belonging to the next region of vertebrae called the *dorsals* or *thoracics*.

Aside from being able to feel some of the cervical spines, you can also feel the bodies of the neck bones. Again, the atlas is different in this regard, because it doesn't have a body. The sides of the cervical bodies are all very palpable and are used as adjusting contact points. It is at these points you'll be able to safely grasp the neck with both hands for either light-force adjusting moves or traction procedures. Make sure you study the diagrams and know where to feel the cervical bodies. Often, when someone is first feeling for the vertebral bodies, they place their fingers too high towards the back of the neck. Notice that the cervical bodies are situated halfway between the back of the neck and the throat. More detail on palpating the bodies is given in the examination chapter.

The most fundamental difference between a cat and human's spinal column is their respective spinal curvatures. A person has two areas in their spine that bend or curve forward (Fig. 3-6). These dips in the spine are called *lordotic curves*, and are located in the

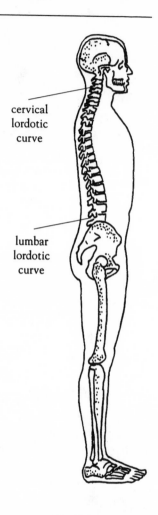

cervical lordotic curve

lumbar lordotic curve

Fig. 3-6.
People have a "small" of their lower back and a similar curve in their neck.

middle to lower part of the neck and also in the lower back, or lumbar region. A cat, like all quadrupeds, has only one of these curves, found at the middle to lower half of the neck. The lordotic curves in both humans and quadrupeds are acquired after birth, soon after walking commences, and are known as *secondary curves*. Compare this to the *primary curve*, which is simply the continuous arch we're all born with, resembling one long dorsal, or outward, curve (Fig. 3-7).

Since cats do not have a secondary lumbar curve, or "small" of their back, they are not prone to the same type of back

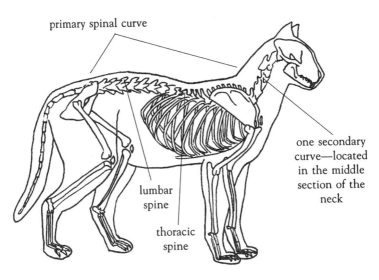

primary spinal curve

one secondary curve—located in the middle section of the neck

lumbar spine

thoracic spine

Fig. 3-7.
A cat, like a dog, has one secondary spinal curve (in its neck). The rest of the spine, from the top of the shoulders all the way to the tail, is one continuous curve.

conditions as people. Lower back disorders found in cats are due to degeneration of a joint often associated with arthritis. This, however, is much more common in dogs and people than with cats.

The Intervertebral Foramen (IVF)

At this point in the spinal anatomy discussion, it is important to note the feature of the spinal column which is most significant to the practice of chiropractic, and that is the *Intervertebral Foramen*, or IVF (Fig. 3-8). The IVF is a small opening or hole formed by two adjacent vertebrae. It is present in all major sections of the spine (cervical, thoracic, and lumbar regions). This opening is the exit for the spinal nerve and other vital structures such as spinal arteries, vertebral veins, and lymphatic vessels. Even a portion of the spinal cord cover (*meninges*) is contained here.

It is the vitality of the IVF that most concerns chiropractors. Tight muscles and ligaments can squeeze the spine, thus crowding the contents of the IVF. When this happens, a spinal nerve's signals become blunted and emit less nerve energy to the intended site (organ). This is the basis of the subluxation theory, or the way a pinched spinal nerve can effect one's overall health. For example, if the spinal nerve leading to the stomach is subluxated, digestion might become disrupted due to abnormal gastric juice production. If any one system in the body is malfunctioning, it puts a strain on the rest of the body, creating even more subluxations and/or compensations. This is why regular chiropractic checkups are necessary: to catch and treat subluxations before they fester into a crisis.

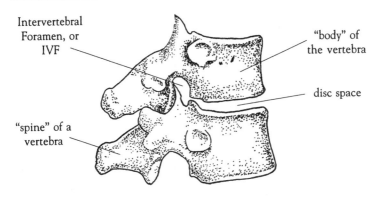

Intervertebral Foramen, or IVF

"body" of the vertebra

disc space

"spine" of a vertebra

Fig. 3-8a.
(Right-side view of two human lumbar vertebrae.) The IVF is the opening for a spinal nerve.

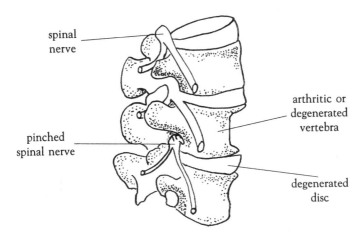

spinal nerve

arthritic or degenerated vertebra

pinched spinal nerve

degenerated disc

Fig. 3-8b.
A dramatic example of a spinal nerve encroached between adjacent vertebrae. **Note:** Chiropractors rarely treat a spinal nerve this badly pinched. This just shows how a spinal nerve can wither if the IVF becomes compromised.

The urgency of keeping the IVF open and biomechanically sound doesn't become apparent to most people unless they experience severe pain, as with sciatica or pain down the leg (Fig. 3-9). The sciatic nerve, which is the thickest nerve of the body, originates from the lower spinal nerves and branches down, supplying the legs with sensory and motor functions. Often, sciatica is caused by an encroachment of the spinal nerve as it leaves the spinal column at the IVF. This encroachment can be caused by a variety of irritating factors, including tight spinal muscles (spasms), joint degeneration, or a herniated disc. Orthopedic surgeons perform operations that are designed to make sure the IVF is clear. One such operation is called a *laminectomy*. This procedure restores the natural opening of the IVF by removing some of the diseased bone tissue (usually caused by arthritic buildup surrounding the lamina) which was blocking that space where the spinal nerve exits. Another operation is called a *discectomy*. Here, the surgeon removes

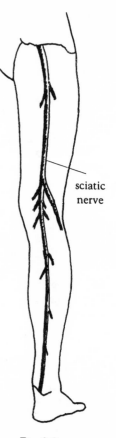

sciatic nerve

Fig. 3-9a.
The large nerve of the leg, the sciatic nerve, can become pinched any place along its course, but is often irritated where it originates—in the lower lumbar region.

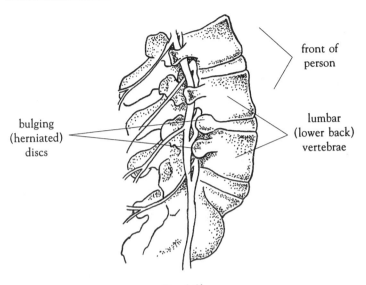

Fig. 3-9b.
(Right side view, human example.) This drawing depicts herniated or bulging discs that are pressing into lower spinal nerves. This will often cause sciatica, or pain down the leg.

part or all of a bulging disc which was also creating a barrier and pressure on the spinal nerve. In each case, these surgeries are necessary—and more often than not, successful—for relieving pain and restoring proper function of the sciatic nerve. **Note:** Chiropractors can also successfully treat sciatica if it is due to nerve pressure caused by muscle spasms constricting the spine. But when there is a mechanical blockage, such as a herniated disc, surgery is usually the most effective and permanent treatment.

The above example of IVF encroachment describes a crisis

situation. The subluxation, however, is much more subtle since pain isn't always involved. Spinal subluxations are of epidemic proportions in both man and beast, and if left untreated, they will eventually cause dis-ease. *The significance of the IVF cannot be overstated.* The above explanation gives examples on how two professions (orthopedic surgeons and chiropractors) both make a living out of keeping the IVF clear.

The Nuchal Ligament

The cat's neck, like that of most quadrupeds, takes on the characteristics of a loaded beam. The cat's neck bones and joints form a horizontal "beam" that must support the weight of the head. A person's head, by contrast, is balanced on their shoulders, an arrangement which is supposedly less prone to injury. However, quadrupeds, including the cat, have a supporting tissue called the *nuchal ligament* which extends from the spine of the axis (second neck bone) to the first thoracic spine (just below the last cervical vertebra) (Fig. 3-10). The nuchal ligament is often regarded as merely a fibrous raphe between the right and left neck muscles. I've often thought of the nuchal ligament as being a "suspension bridge" between the mid-back and the head. It is important to know the location of this ligament, since neck problems can sometimes start there. Tight muscle surrounding the nuchal ligament often signify additional neck spasms and subluxations in other areas of the spine. If your cat is unable to turn his head to the right, for example, feel for tight neck muscles on the right of the nuchal ligament. The neck is often referred to as the "second" pair of eyes, since proper neck motion allows a wider field of vision.

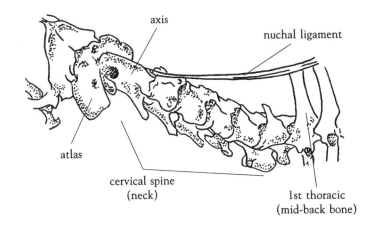

Fig. 3-10.
(Left-side view of the cat's neck.) The nuchal ligament.

Thoracics (Mid-Back Bones)

The cat has 13 mid-back bones or thoracic vertebrae, also known as dorsals (Fig. 3-11). Each of these vertebrae has a "spine" that can be felt on the top (dorsal aspect) of its back; these are used as adjusting contact points. Like the cervicals, each thoracic has a vertebral body. However, unlike the cervicals, the vertebral bodies of the thoracics and lumbars cannot be felt. The joints of the thoracic spine are less tightly connected than ours. This feature is what allows the cat to arch its back into a "U" shape during defensive situations.

Study the diagrams and note the angle of the thoracic spines. The top ones point *caudally*, or towards the tail. This *imbrication* or "shingling" quality is important to note when

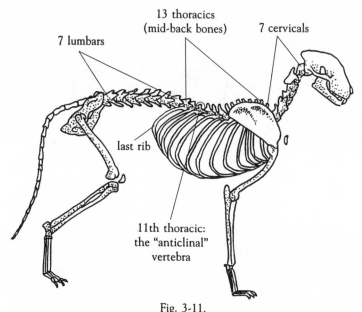

Fig. 3-11.

All of the thoracics are bound by ribs. The lumbars, or lower-back vertebrae, begin directly below the last rib. **Note:** This diagram points out the eleventh thoracic (dorsal) vertebra. Its spine is shorter than the adjacent vertebrae and will sometimes feel as though it is "missing."

applying a chiropractic thrust (impulse). Some chiropractic techniques require the practitioner to push down on one of these spines while performing an adjustment. During manipulative procedures, the thrust should always compliment the direction or angle of each individual spine, which lessens the shearing force on the vertebral joints. Simply stated, the adjustment is smoother when you follow this rule.

As you'll learn in the method chapters, your adjusting hand

or thumb acts as an extension of each spine. Thus, for the upper thoracics, you're not pushing straight down, but caudal to cranial, which means in the direction from the tail to the head (Fig. 3-12). This, however, changes as the directions of the thoracic spines change. Note that this overlapping or downward sloping of the spines stops when you reach the eleventh thoracic. The eleventh thoracic is known as the *anticlinal* vertebra, and signifies the end of imbrication. Furthermore, the eleventh thoracic spine is shorter than the others and will feel like a depression in the cat's back when you palpate the surrounding spines. People feeling their cat's back for the first time may mistake this depression for an injury, not knowing this is normal anatomy. After the anticlinal vertebra, the remaining two thoracic spines point up and even slightly towards the head (cranial).

Also note from the diagrams that ribs are attached to each thoracic vertebra, which makes the thoracic spine as a whole feel much more rigid or supported than the cervical or lumbar regions. The thoracics are the only vertebrae that attach to ribs, with the exception of the occasional *cervical rib,* which attaches to the last neck bone.

Lumbars (Lower Back Bones)

The cat has seven lumbars, or lower back bones. The spines of the lumbars look and feel much like the lower two thoracic spines, and the lumbar curve is the same as the thoracic curve. If it weren't for the ribs, you might think the lumbars were an extension of the thoracics.

There's an additional set of adjusting contact points found

Fig. 3-12a.
When adjusting the mid- and lower-back vertebrae, your adjusting arm is essentially an extension of the spinous process or "spine." That is, when a spinous points downward, so do your hand, wrist, and elbow.

Fig. 3-12b.
Adjusting the cat with the metal mallet. **Note:** The mallet, again, is like an extension of the spinous process and should angle down in the same direction.

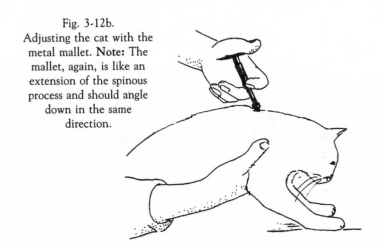

on the lumbars: the *mammillary processes* (Figs. 3-13 and 3-14). These little bumps are found at the sides of the lumbar (and lower thoracic) spines. Keep this in mind when you study the methods.

Sacrum

The sacrum, which is composed of three fused bones, is often thought of as a continuation of the spine. However, it cannot be palpated from the back, since it is wedged too deeply between the two pelvic bones (Fig. 3-14). The tip or *sacral apex* can be felt by lifting up the tail and feeling the area just above the anus (Fig. 3-15)—see the Ligament Push (Logan Basic Technique) in Chapter 15.

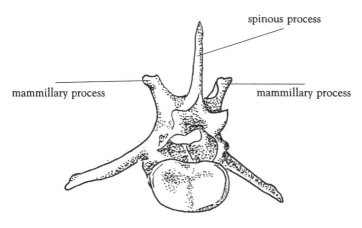

Fig. 3-13.
(Lumbar vertebra, as seen from behind.) The mammillary processes of the lower thoracics and lumbars can be used as adjusting contact points.

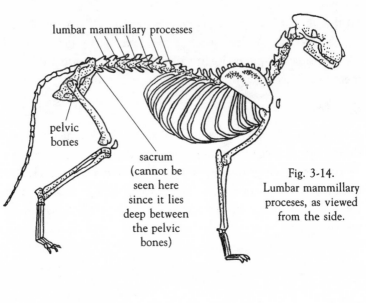

lumbar mammillary processes

pelvic
bones

sacrum
(cannot be
seen here
since it lies
deep between
the pelvic
bones)

Fig. 3-14.
Lumbar mammillary
proceses, as viewed
from the side.

Fig. 3-15.
The sacrum, which is the bone
directly below the last lumbar,
can opnly be felt at the "apex"
by lifting the tail and feeling a
spot deep and above the first
tail bone.

contact point for the
Logan Basic
Technique

anus

The Tail Bones (Coccygeal or Caudal Vertebrae)

An average of 20 separate bones make up the cat's tail. The tail itself is often adjusted, but it usually acts as a handle to aid in adjusting other parts of the spine and during traction procedures.

Though not seen as frequently with cats as with dogs, tail bobbing and ear clipping surgeries are nothing short of mutilation. By removing these vital tissues that nature had intended, the animal may experience a phenomenon called *phantom pain*, or *pseudesthesia*, which is more maddening than real pain since the "pain" can never be resolved. Phantom pain or sensation is when a person loses an arm, for example, but still senses that it itches or burns, since the brain still contains a memory of the lost limb. Also, by removing ear parts, important acupuncture points are also lost. There is a branch of acupuncture called *auricular therapy* that utilizes ear points only. This, too, applies to animals. Therefore, by clipping away part of the ear, the animal is deprived of a viable alternative treatment.

Discs

Between each pair of vertebrae, except the first two neck bones, is a *disc*. A disc is a fibrous ligament that contains a fluid center called the *nucleus pulposus* (Fig. 3-16). The purpose of the disc is to give shape to the spine, separate the vertebrae, and absorb shock while walking and jumping. The disc is also the site of many types of back conditions, since it is somewhat prone to injury. A "slipped" or ruptured disc, for example, is when the fluid center (nucleus) bursts out of the surrounding fiber and

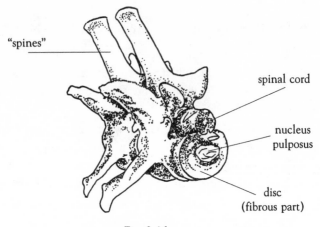

Fig. 3-16.
A human example of the nucleus pulposus of a disc.

oozes into a spinal nerve (see Fig. 3-9b).

The chiropractic practitioner should use caution when treating a cat with a herniated disc. When chiropractic treatment is indicated for disc conditions, light, soft-tissue methods are preferred to spinal manipulation. **Note:** Routine X-rays are not sufficient to diagnose disc conditions. Regular X-rays are mainly good for diagnosing bones and teeth, which are tissues containing calcium, a metallic substance. Discs are soft tissues (fibrocartilage) and do not contain calcium. What *can* be seen on plain X-rays are disc spaces. When a disc ruptures and/or degenerates, a smaller disc space will be present on an x-ray between adjacent vertebrae. An MRI (magnetic resonance imaging) examination, which does not utilize X-rays, is very accurate in diagnosing disc and other soft-tissue diseases. Another accurate test used to diagnose soft tissues (and I knew I'd mention this sooner or later) is the CAT *scan* (computerized axial tomography). The CAT scan, however, does utilize ionizing radiation.

Hips (Pelvic Bones)

The hips can be felt at the back end of your cat, directly above the thighs and around the sacrum (Fig 3-17). The two most important hip adjusting points are located near the top of the two pelvic bones. These points are called the *posterior-superior-iliac spines* (PSIS) and are used for a lot of lower back moves (Fig. 3-18). Another area of the hip used in adjusting is the hip socket, or *acetabular joint*. This is where the head of the femur

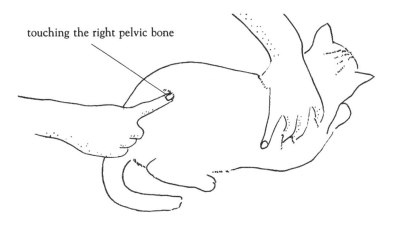

touching the right pelvic bone

Fig. 3-17.
The top of each pelvic bone can be felt here. **Note:** Do not confuse this with the hip socket (shown later).

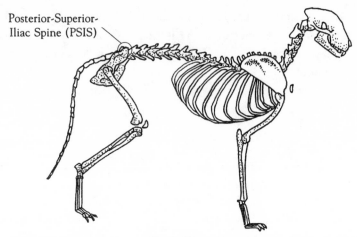

Posterior-Superior-Iliac Spine (PSIS)

Fig. 3-18.
The PSIS is an important contact point on the pelvis, since it acts as a lever which makes adjusting the pelvis easier.

(thigh bone) fits into the hip socket. Dogs, though not cats, have a common problem here called *hip dysplasia*. Canine hip dysplasia is usually a congenital condition where the ball-and-socket configuration of the thigh bone as it fits into the hip is not functionally sound (Fig. 3-19). This is due to a shallow socket. It may be of interest to note that when a hip replacement is recommended for dogs with hip dysplasia (or for that matter, people with walking problems), the hip *joint* is replaced, not the pelvic bones.

Cats do not develop hip dysplasia, but they can and do suffer from hip conditions caused by joint degeneration. A feline hip condition that looks like canine hip dysplasia is *avascular necrosis*. Here, blood supply to the hip socket is cut

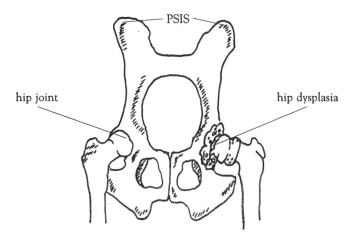

Fig. 3-19.
Canine hip dysplasia.

off, usually due to falling injuries, and the bone tissue dies. This causes the cat to limp and favor the affected side. The treatment for avascular necrosis is surgery. If you know your cat fell from a high platform, have its hips checked by your vet. Sometimes early detection and physical therapy can arrest this condition and surgery may be avoided.

OTHER BONES

The Head

The shape of the cat's head is designed for hunting. It has a powerful mouth, searing teeth, sensitive ears, and eyes that work very well in dim light. But as powerful as its mouth is, the cat doesn't chew at all—it swallows its food whole. The cat has 30 teeth which are predominantly made for cutting meat. (For the record, a dog has 42 teeth.) It's interesting to note that a cat cannot survive on a pure vegetarian diet. A cat who is deprived of meat will die within a year. Dogs, however, can live on an all-vegetarian diet (but they will not thrive on it).

The two features of the cat's head that are relevant to the practice of chiropractic is their lack of a long (dog-like) snout, and their *Temporomandibular Joint* (TMJ), or jaw joint (Fig. 3-20).

Most dogs have a long snout you can grasp like a handle which is used during some neck adjustments. With cats, you must grasp the entire face like a doorknob for similar neck

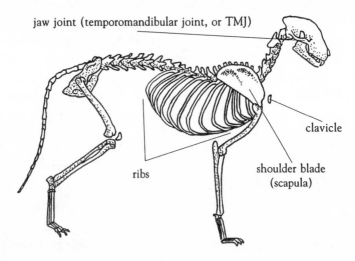

jaw joint (temporomandibular joint, or TMJ)

clavicle

ribs

shoulder blade
(scapula)

Fig. 3-20.
The jaw joint (TMJ), ribs, and shoulder blades are frequently adjusted.

methods (but make sure the cat was fed recently and has a sense of humor).

As for the TMJ, cats can have problems all their own. Since they don't chew, they don't move their jaw laterally (side-to-side, like a cow or dog), just up and down. So a cat with a TMJ condition will show a laterally deviated jaw, listing to one side or the other, since that would be abnormal.

The Scapula

The *scapulas*, or shoulder blades, are flat bones located on each side of the spine, hugging the upper ribs (see Fig. 3-20). The high point of the scapula can be felt below the last neck bone at the level of the first or second thoracic "spine." The scapula does not form a true joint with the upper limbs; rather, it is loosely positioned in its boundaries by muscle attachments.

Though not vertebrae, the scapulas are considered by most animal chiropractors to be important adjusting sites. This is because the cat, like all quadrupeds, carry more than half of their body weight on the front half of the body (shoulder joints) while walking. People carry all of their body weight on their hips.

For all practical purposes, cats do not have *clavicles* or collarbones. (While these bones are present, they are extremely small and buried in muscle tissue.) A cat doesn't need this bone, which is normally used to lift the forearm outward. The lack of a collarbone allows cats to squeeze through tight places since the presence of one would broaden its chest. Also, without a clavicle, a cat is able to run faster with less restriction.

Ribs

A cat has 13 pairs of ribs, attached to the spine (thoracics) in the back and to the sternum in front (see Fig. 3-20). Cats have a narrow chest, so never allow the chest to absorb an adjusting thrust. For some mid-back adjustments, you'll be supporting your cat's chest with your other hand instead of having the cat lie sprawled on its belly (Fig. 3-21). Since the ribs attach to the spine, you may mistake a misaligned vertebrae for a subluxated rib head. In these cases, do not manipulate the vertebrae, but rather, use light massage techniques and pressure points. Also, labored breathing is a sign of rib and mid back pain.

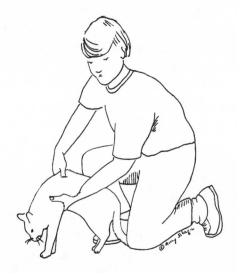

Fig. 3-21.
For some thoracic adjustments, the cat is supported under his chest—not sprawled on the floor.

Forelimbs

You can see from the skeletal diagrams (Fig. 3-22) that cats' bones are similar to ours. We each have a *humerus* (upper arm), and in the lower arm, the *radius* (thumb side) and *ulna* (pinky side). Where the ulna and radius meet the humerus is the elbow joint. As you look further down the arm you'll find the wrist bones (*carpus*), and below that, the finger or toe bones (*phalanges*).

Cats can have problems with their wrists, but not the same kind as humans. People who overuse their wrists (e.g., working on a word processor) can become afflicted with a condition

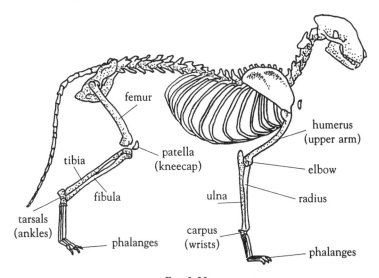

Fig. 3-22.
The cat's skeleton is similar to that of humans; all of the bones named here are common to both cats and humans.

known as *carpal tunnel syndrome*. This is where a large nerve of the arm (the *median nerve*) gets trapped within the inflamed "rock garden" formed by the irregular array of carpal bones, causing pain, numbness, and weakness in the affected hand. Cats use their front legs as rudders and frequently stress their wrists during tight maneuvering and running on uneven terrain. As you'll see in Chapter 16, there are easy adjusting methods for the carpus.

Hind Limbs

Again, you will find similarities between people and cats while studying the hind legs. Each has a thigh bone (*femur*), and two lower (shin) bones, the *tibia* and the *fibula*. The knee is formed where the femur and the two shin bones meet. There is even a knee cap (*patella*) present at this junction. Cats and humans each have ankle bones (*tarsals*) and toes (*phalanges*). But the main difference between cats and people is that cats walk and run on their toes. Notice that the cat's ankle bone (or *hock*) points up. This would normally be our heel! When a person wants to run fast, they sprint on their toes. A cat does this all the time. That's one reason they're such efficient runners.

A joint that bends (flexes or closes) and straightens (extends or opens) with minimal effort, such as the ones formed by the long bones (front and hind limbs), is considered normal even with the presence or expression of pain.

The Muscles

Muscles are soft fibrous tissues that contract and produce body movements when energized by nerve impulses. They also give the body bulk and shape, and can become knotted in response to sudden movements.

There are three types of muscles in the body: *smooth muscles*, found in blood vessels and hollow organs; *cardiac muscles*, found only in the heart; and *skeletal muscles* (a.k.a. voluntary muscles), which attach to the bones and account for more than half of your cat's body weight. Wherever you see a reference to muscles in this book, we're discussing skeletal muscles. All areas of your cat's body is covered by skeletal muscles ranging in size from the very minute eye muscles to the bulky rump muscles.

Muscles are able to perform work because they are attached to bones by tendons. There are generally two places a muscle attaches to a bone: the *origin* or more fixed point; and the *insertion*, the more moveable point, found further down the bone.

You can think of the musculoskeletal system as a series of puppets in a marionette show: the puppet being the bones and the strings being the muscles. The puppet would not be able to move in any meaningful way if the strings were not attached in strategic areas. This is precisely the relationship the bones have with the muscles. This is also the basis for spotting lameness.

When you suffer a sprained neck, the first thing you notice is pain, because your neck is restricted. One of the strings is too tight and can't do its job. But this isn't all bad. Your body doesn't give you anything you don't need. A muscle spasm is simply a natural body splint that stops your body in motion to prevent further injury. People who pay attention to this warning signal and stop lifting weights for a week will mend faster. In this sense, cats are smarter than people. When a cat suffers a severe muscle cramp, it will lie down for a while and let its muscles heal, since it doesn't fear getting fired for skipping work.

The bones are a series of levers that are moved by muscles. Proper movement of joints is produced by muscles working in harmony. When your body is in motion, some muscles relax while others contract. A muscle that is stretched or massaged before an athletic event is less likely to sustain injury, because it can adapt to sudden movements better than a stiff muscle. Cats are natural "stretchers" and know the importance of keeping limber.

The muscle diagrams (Fig. 3-23) are here to give you an idea of the size and location of the major muscles. Study these diagrams while holding your cat and try to feel the different directions of the striations (fibers). Knowing the direction of the fibers is important when applying pressure-point or massage methods. If you want to "clean out" a muscle and help it heal after an injury, massage *against the grain of the muscle fibers* for about two minutes per muscle knot, up to five treatments per week. This technique is called Transverse Friction Massage (TFM). An injured muscle needs a constant flow of blood and lymph in order to rebuild itself, and TFM helps the muscle attain this.

A muscle area that feels thick and fleshy is called the *belly*, which is the center of the muscle (between the origin and insertion). This is the site of most muscle knots and trigger points. The method chapters will teach you ways you can accomplish most pain treatments by simply pressing your finger into a muscle knot.

Whenever you examine your cat's muscles, feel them in all postures—that is, standing, sitting, relaxed, flexed, or extended—and in as many actions as possible. An injured or spastic muscle will restrict movement in several postures. This is particularly important while feeling the muscles near the spine. Learn to

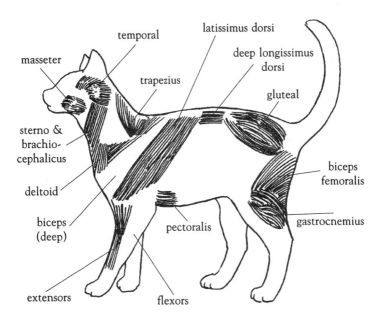

Fig. 3-23.
Cat muscles. Note the direction of the fibers or striations.

feel the difference between a hard, inelastic bone (i.e., ribs) and a hard muscle. At first touch they may feel the same, but by moving your finger back and forth and a little deeper, you'll notice the difference; a muscle feels stringier than a hard bone. Also, a cat will display more pain when you probe a muscle.

THE NERVES

It is because of a condition caused by a pinched nerve that chiropractic got its start. The year was 1895. The first chiropractic patient, a janitor named Harvey Lillard, complained of hearing loss when he sought the help of Dr. Daniel David Palmer, a magnetic healer who practiced in Davenport, Iowa. Mr. Lillard told Dr. Palmer that he had injured his back seventeen years earlier while working, and had had diminished hearing ever since. When Dr. Palmer examined Mr. Lillard's spine, he felt a misaligned vertebra, and then preceded to "rack it" into place (after which, Dr. Palmer probably experienced some hearing loss of his own). This was the first chiropractic adjustment—and it restored Mr. Lillard's hearing.

Whether or not the above story is based on 100% fact, the world may never know. But the truth is, nerves are everywhere in the body, and their connections are widespread. It is entirely possible that a pinched spinal nerve can affect hearing. The chiropractic subluxation theory is based on the fact that spinal nerves can be pinched between the vertebrae and that this causes distress to the related muscle or organ.

The nervous system is divided into two parts: the *central nervous system*, which includes your brain and spinal cord, and the *peripheral nervous system*, which includes everything else (Fig. 3-24). The spinal nerves are part of the peripheral nervous system, and the spine is the area most often treated by chiropractors for pinched nerves. The spine is the switchboard of the body. Every neurological transmission, whether coming from the body to the brain (*afferent pathways*) or from the brain to the body (*efferent pathways*), must pass through the spine. A blockage of these signals will impair body-to-brain communication and cause disease. Chiropractic strives to maintain body communication.

There is frequently a confusion of terms relating to the back, especially the differences between the *spinal cord*, the

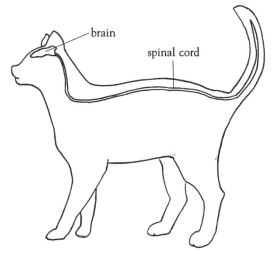

Fig. 3-24.
The central nervous system includes the brain and spinal cord. All the other nerves in the body are referred to as peripheral nerves.

spinal column, and *spinal nerves*. The spinal cord is nerve tissue protected within the spinal column (back bones or vertebrae), much as the brain is protected by the skull. Spinal nerves are long nerves that originate in the spinal cord and pass through openings in the spinal column, making their way to the rest of the body (Fig. 3-25).

The part of the peripheral nervous system over which you have little or no control is called the *autonomic nervous system*. The "autonomics," also referred to as the *involuntary* and/or *vegetative nervous system*, control your breathing while you sleep, your heart rate, and your glandular functions, to name a few.

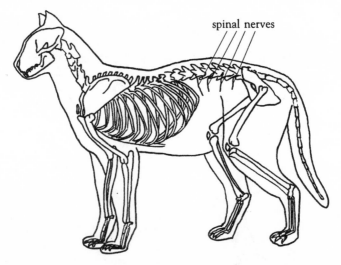

spinal nerves

Fig. 3-25.
The spinal nerves originate from the spinal cord, pass through the hole created by two adjacent vertebrae (the IVF), and make their way to an organ, muscle, etc.

This part of the nervous system is particularly important because your cat may not show any signs of distress; conditions of the autonomics are mostly silent until they culminate into a crisis in the form of muscle spasms or internal dis-ease. This is why you must always check your cat's spine for subluxations. Stop problems before they happen. Practice maintenance care.

For those concerned mostly about lameness in their cat (problems with gait), you should know that the spinal nerves located at the upper part of your cat's back control his front legs. The low-back spinal nerves control his hind legs. The mid-back spinal nerves control the surrounding muscles. Almost the entire range of spinal nerves regulates internal organs in some way.

You cannot feel pinched spinal nerves, but you can make an educated guess on their specific locations by knowing what ails your cat. If you vet has diagnosed a stomach condition, look for areas on the spine that relate to the stomach (see charts). You'll also learn from the examination chapter that true subluxations or pinched spinal nerves have a few things in common. Some of the most common signs of vertebral subluxation include restricted joint motion over the painful area, a hard muscle knot next to a "spine," and increased heat on that hard knot.

For those less experienced with examining pets, the first thing you'll notice is that all of your pets (dogs or cats) feel warmer. A healthy cat's temperature is about 101.5°F (compared to 98.6°F for people). Get used to feeling the warmth of the whole cat before you start isolating prospective trouble spots. It takes experience and a sensitive touch to distinguish warm spots from hot spots, mainly because the fur is a barrier to the skin (except on the hairless Manx).

Physical Differences Between Dogs and Cats

The most obvious physical difference between dogs and cats is size variation. Cats basically come in one size, between 6 and 15 pounds, the most common weight being 12 pounds. Dogs, in contrast, differ greatly by size. By some estimates there are over 2000 distinct breeds of dogs, and about 130 recognized breeds of domestic cats. The weight range of dog breeds varies from less than 3 pounds (Chihuahua) to over 200 pounds (Saint Bernard). No other species of mammal differs this much in weight and size in terms of magnitude (about 100 times).

Another striking difference between cats and dogs is the number of bones each has in its body. Dogs are listed as having about 319 bones, while cats are said to have about 244. Why such a big discrepancy? What bones do dogs have that cats don't? I asked Dr. Mark Simon, an associate professor at the University of Illinois' veterinary college in Champaign, IL, to answer this for me. What Dr. Simon told me is that it's all in the counting. Dogs and cats actually do have about the same number of bones. But cats are often used in human biology classes, and for the sake of brevity, the eight bones of the pelvis, for example, are lumped together and counted as one. Other examples of multiple-bone areas counted as one include the skull and the sternum.

Dr. Simon also shared other bits of "and now you know" information about cats, namely the cheetah. Dr. Simon explained that the cheetah can run faster than any other cat (or land mammal) because they are missing a structure called the *posterior scapular ligament.* This ligament, which is found on all other cats, acts to "strap down" a section of the shoulder bone (scapula), thus limiting foreleg extension. Dr. Simon also pointed out that if you watch the cheetah run (preferably compliments of the TV show *National Geographic*), you'll notice their shoulder blades rotating almost like propellers. The shoulder blades of lions and tigers appear to be more constricted while running.

Cats and dogs do have one thing in common; the *tapetum lucidum*, a membrane layer in the eye that is capable of reflecting light. This is why their eyes appear to be a metallic green or gold in dim light and why they can see well in the dark. It may be of interest to some that the tapetum lucidum also exists in one group of people—the aboriginal people of Australia.

Cats have something dogs could really use: the *righting reflex.* Cats are able to turn around in midair and land on their feet when dropped. This is probably the best reason why cats don't experience lameness nearly as often as dogs.

Those who have owned both cats and dogs know that dogs do not have retractable claws, but cats do. The retractable claws in cats are mainly used for climbing, fighting, and hunting. The only member of the cat family lacking retractable claws is the cheetah. In this writer's opinion, there are no good reasons to have a cats' claws removed, especially just to protect inanimate objects.

Other miscellaneous differences between cats and dogs: A cat has a faster heart rate than a dog (110–180 beats per minute, or bpm, vs. 70–130 bpm respectively). A cat also has a higher respiration rate compared to dogs (30–50 breaths per minute vs. 10–30 breaths per minute, respectively). Both cats and dogs have body temperatures of about 101.3–101.5°F, and they have similar gestation times (about 60 days).

Some may be interested to know that a cat's purr does *not* come from its larynx, but from the vibration of blood in a large blood vessel (carotid artery) in the chest cavity. However, the air-filled bronchial tubes and windpipe aid in the overall sound and resonance of the purr. Kittens use the purring vibration as a homing device from their mother, since their own senses of sight and sound are underdeveloped.

The next chapter describes the examination procedure as it applies to arriving at a chiropractic diagnosis, or more accurately, an opinion. **Note:** This book will not make doctors out of cat owners who are not doctors already. It merely gives you a limited working knowledge of feline chiropractic methods that you *may* use at your own discretion, in the absence of professional chiropractic care.

CHAPTER 4

WHAT'S THAT POPPING NOISE? (THE DYNAMICS AND TOOLS OF CAT ADJUSTING)

O*h, I can't watch. I can't watch. I'm leaving the room. No—wait. Wait until I'm gone. Ahhhhhhhh!! I hate the sound of someone's bones crunching.*"

How many times have I heard this from a bystander observing an adjustment? And it's usually an acquaintance who came to give their friend moral support! Stay away from people like this. If someone from this crowd saw a man standing on the ledge of a 40-story building, they'd be the first one to yell "jump."

Frankly, I don't like to hear the sound of bones crunching either during the adjustment. Bones should not, and *do not*, crunch during a chiropractic treatment. Crunching would imply that something broke, which is what the chiropractor would be if something ever did.

So then, what is it? What is that confounded sound that some people fear during the adjustment? And more importantly, is that sound necessary to assure you the adjustment was made?

The noise you feel and hear during an adjustment is gas escaping from a suddenly opened joint. This is comparable to the sound made when you pull (as opposed to slide) a small rubber suction cup away from a flat piece of glass, as are often used with fish tanks to hold up the filters. This is also the same noise people experience when they "pop" their knuckles.* And as any knuckle-popper knows, you can't always pop them at will. You have to wait a while before you're able to pop again. The reason is because the refractory period, which is the time needed to "refill" the joints with gas, is about twenty minutes.

Chiropractic is a conscious energy release from the practitioner to the patient for the purpose of removing nerve irritation that can cause dis-ease. The word "dis-ease" is frequently hyphenated in chiropractic texts to denote *lack of ease* in the body as oppose to a specific pathology. Once the nerve irritation has been removed, the body can function at full capacity. The number of visits required to correct a subluxation or nerve interference largely depends on the fortitude of the patient's musculoskeletal system. In my experience, a subluxated cat who can be helped with chiropractic usually responds favorably within one to four visits over a two-week period. There are, of course, exceptions. But in general, if a condition doesn't respond to conservative treatment within five weeks or less, then something else is wrong and the patient should be referred to a doctor who uses more aggressive therapies.

---

* Habitual knuckle-popping does *not* cause arthritis, as some would have you believe. Arthritis is largely an inherited disease. However, constant popping does make the ligaments between your fingers looser, perpetuating the continual need for this release.

Different Approaches

Chiropractors use several ways to deliver the energy, thrust, or impulse that is called a chiropractic adjustment. There are as many chiropractic styles as there are makes of cars on the road (over a hundred), but the outcome is the same—they all get you there. Surprisingly, most of the chiropractic techniques do *not* involve joint popping. Some very effective methods are nothing more than a light touch on the skin. Therefore, joint noise is not a requirement for a successful adjustment.

Exploring every possible cat-adjusting method here would be not only impractical, but also confusing. I have therefore selected a few practical, easy-to-administer procedures that require some, but not a lot of practice (unless otherwise marked "Professional Expertise Required"). For most of these methods you will simply use your hands to deliver the adjustment or tissue manipulation. There are some people who prefer an instrument called a *metal mallet* (a.k.a. *activator*) to deliver the thrust.

The metal mallet (Fig. 4-1) is a chiropractic tool that delivers a *sudden* but *low-force* impulse into a joint. It is considered very safe and effective when properly used. The force of the thrust can be controlled by varying the number of "rings" at the top of the instrument (see the instructions in Chapter 10). A healthy percentage of chiropractors base their entire practice, human or otherwise, on using this device. There are, however, those cat owners who prefer the good old hands-on-only approach to their pet. To perform the more traditional

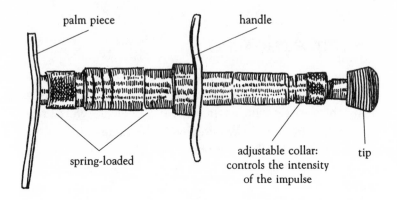

palm piece   handle

spring-loaded

adjustable collar:
controls the intensity
of the impulse

tip

Fig. 4-1.
The metal mallet, or activator, is a well-accepted and safe chiropractic
adjusting tool. It emits a light to moderate thrust/impulse when the
handle is squeezed.

methods of feline chiropractic as well as those methods utilizing the metal mallet, it is essential to understand some adjusting fundamentals.

THE ADJUSTING THRUST

Let's shed a myth right here. "The only people capable of
delivering a good, hearty chiropractic adjustment are those big,
blond health club rats with fifteen-inch biceps." I frequently
hear statements like this, especially when I mention that even
horses can be adjusted by hand only and without the use of
sledgehammers. As in many of life's situations, our beliefs are
deeply shrouded by myth and are ingrained in our minds since
youth.

The chiropractic thrust is based on speed, not a hard force (high velocity, low amplitude). The hand-held metal mallet (activator) fits this description. Your own hands and arms are also equipped to deliver a safe adjustment, providing you have normal muscle coordination and finger dexterity. This is very similar to the physics governing martial arts such as karate. How else could a 110-pound person split ten thick wooden boards with one blow?

Types Of Manual Adjusting

1. **Set and Hold.** A set and hold adjustment is when your hands stay at the end-point position after the adjustment. When adjusting a person's mid-back, for example, the chiropractor stands above his patient with his elbows slightly flexed so he has some "slack" to spend to deliver the adjustment (Fig. 4-2). At the end of the adjustment, his elbows stay fully extended, holding the vertebra down with his hands. This prevents the vertebra from recoiling.

2. **Toggle Recoil.** This is the opposite of the set and hold maneuver. Here the adjustment starts off the same (flexed elbows), and the sudden thrust is made, but the elbows quickly return to the original flexed position allowing the vertebra to find its own level—its original "home." This type of adjustment is usually performed on the atlas (the first neck bone), since it is a ring-like vertebra with flexible boundaries and has the ability to oscillate with a dynamic thrust.

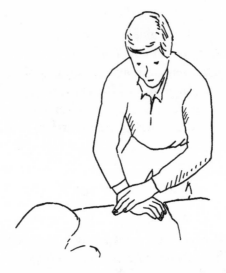

Fig. 4-2.
For most human mid-back adjustments, the chiropractor stans above his patient with his elbows slightly flexed before delivering the adjustment.

3. **Pressure Point Contacts.** There are some techniques that simply require the practitioner to feel for a hard muscle and apply steady pressure into it with their finger. You should be able to judge the right amount of pressure to use so as not to stress a joint or injure a muscle. Knowing joint limitations is helpful as well. For example, some neck methods will ask you to place the knife edge of your index finger on a mid-cervical and bend the cat's neck over that finger. When you feel increasing tension between the cat's neck and your finger, you have to know when to stop pressing.

Stabilization

Basically, the chiropractic usage of stabilization means keeping the patient or part of the patient still during the adjustment. A person who is getting an adjustment can lie prone (face down) on a special chiropractic table so their chest is stabilized while their mid-back is being treated. Since cats are small, the practitioner's leg often acts as the table for the adjustment. Other times, one section of the spine must be kept from moving while another segment is being worked on. For example, if you want to adjust the last lumbar only, your stabilizing hand would then keep the above lumbars from moving. This way, your thrust is singularly directed to the subluxated vertebra and is more specific.

Chapter 5

Lameness Or Illness?
(The Pre~Chiropractic
Evaluation)

Before you evaluate your cat for subluxations and abnormal joint motion, as described in the following chapter, you should be familiar with some disorders that appear to be caused by injury, but are actually something completely different. In this chapter, we will explore information which is vital to the overall chiropractic evaluation of your cat. I would like to alert you to certain "red flags" which will enable you to differentiate between physical conditions that can be helped with chiropractic care and ones that cannot. Some of these illnesses would be considered *contraindications*, which are reason not to adjust or to use extreme caution if you do (see Chapter 8).

Animal chiropractors primarily treat assorted types of lameness. Lameness is often due to injury—or, at times, to a pinched spinal nerve—usually affecting the limbs while walking and running. Conditions associated with a faulty gait are easy to see, even with an untrained eye. But cats are unique. They do not suffer nearly as much from musculoskeletal conditions as dogs do. Some veterinarians postulate that this is because cats are, in general, much more flexible than dogs, and therefore more resilient to trauma (hence, nine lives). A cat exhibiting a labored gait or neck stiffness, for example, is likely to be suffering from a genetic musculoskeletal disorder coupled by a nutritional deficiency, rather than impairments due to injury. This, however, does not mean that chiropractic would not be beneficial to the cat. On the contrary, cats who suffer from disabilities caused by internal conditions need chiropractic care even more. So just for the moment, you must separate feline medical conditions from vertebral subluxations, then integrate the two once you've read Chapters 6 and 7.

FELINE MUSCULOSKELETAL SYSTEM DISORDERS (AND RELATED METABOLIC DISEASES)

Musculoskeletal disorders not caused by trauma are associated with other underlying problems. Some of these problems include metabolic conditions, infections, inflammatory diseases, or congenital afflictions. In rarer cases, neoplastic (cancerous tumors) diseases may be present. Metabolic diseases, such as the ones mentioned below, are due to an imbalance in the normal physiological processes of the body. Whatever the disease, your vet is the only one who should make the diagnosis and prescribe treatment.

Hypervitaminosis A

The condition known as hypervitaminosis A is caused by too much vitamin A in the diet. Since vitamin A is stored in the liver, an all-liver diet will bring on the characteristics of this disease. One such characteristic includes *deforming cervical spondylosis*, which causes the neck bones (cervical vertebrae) to fuse together, restricting the cat's ability to flex (bend) its neck. There is also an associated occurrence of bony outgrowths that can be felt on the cervical vertebrae, which can damage associated spinal nerve roots.

The toxicity of consuming too much vitamin A can also result in the fusion of other joints such as the elbow. (These bone and joint deformities cannot be reversed, but a better balanced diet can help reduce the pain.) If a cat's joints are immobile (*ankylosis*), its ability to groom itself is impeded, thus poor hair quality is noticed. Weight loss may also be attributed to this disease, since eating becomes painful. You'll also notice the cat's skin is sensitive and doesn't want to be touched. This, coupled with the bony changes, are reasons enough not to use spinal manipulation on the affected parts. Instead, use the more gentle soft-tissue methods when chiropractic care is indicated.

Nutritional Secondary Hyperparathyroidism

Calcium is one of the most important minerals of the body. Aside from being essential for a normal metabolism, calcium—together with fluoride, phosphorus, and magnesium—forms the hard structure of bones and teeth.

Nutritional secondary hyperparathyroidism is, for all practical purposes, a calcium deficiency caused by an all-meat diet, which is high in phosphorus but low in calcium. Even though cats are true carnivores, they need calcium to stay healthy. (Canned fish often contains chopped-up bones, so it is a good source of calcium—as is milk.) In the wild, cats get calcium by eating not only the meat from their prey, but some of the bones as well. The primary result of calcium deficiency is brittle bones, which become demineralized. This is because a lack of calcium in the diet will cause the *parathyroid glands* (Fig. 5-1) to secrete *parathyroid hormone* (PTH), which helps extract calcium from the cats' bones, causing them to become thin and brittle. This can be detected by an X-ray exam.

The signs of this disease include weakness or limping (from possible fractures), bowing of the legs, abnormal spinal curvatures, and vertebral compression, which can result in nerve damage. The signs of nerve damage would be paralysis and incoordination of the limbs (*ataxia*), and paralysis of the bladder from spinal cord compression. If this disease is detected early, improvement can occur if the diet is changed to include calcium. Again, soft-tissue chiropractic methods should be used here, and are often helpful for temporary relief of pain.

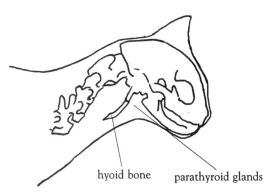

hyoid bone   parathyroid glands

Fig. 5-1.
The parathyroid glands are located in the throat, near the hyoid bone.

Renal Secondary Hyperparathyroidism

Renal secondary hyperparathyroidism is another kind of calcium deficiency disease—not because the cat didn't eat enough calcium, but because its kidneys were malfunctioning. This could be due to a number of reasons, including congenital abnormalities or other diseases. If your vet has diagnosed this condition but is still unsure of the cause, then check your cat's spine for subluxations near the area that controls kidney function (the lower spine). You might be surprised to find areas of muscle tightness there.

Hypokalemic Polymyopathy

Potassium is also needed for normal metabolism. With hypokalemic polymyopathy, potassium is depleted. This is partially due to malfunctioning kidneys and a low-potassium diet. The signs of this disorder include muscle weakness, a stiffened posture, and difficulty raising the head due to weak muscles. Adding additional potassium to the diet can reverse these signs. (Fortunately, most commercial cat foods and snacks are fortified with potassium—even the more natural brands.)

Other Diseases That Cause Lameness

As you might expect, cats suffer from many of the same joint diseases as people. Arthritis is one them. Arthritis is simply inflammation of a joint (*artho-* refers to joints, and *-itis* means "inflammation"). The type of arthritis most frequently seen in cats that causes lameness is *osteoarthritis* (a.k.a. degenerative joint disease). Osteoarthritis is commonly associated with aging, but other factors, such as trauma and prolonged athletic training, contribute to its severity. Arthritis is generally exacerbated by exercise and cold, damp weather. People often take aspirin to ease arthritic pain and inflammation. However, cats should *not* be given aspirin, since it may be toxic to them. Always consult your vet before administering any medication.

A less common cause of feline lameness is *osteomyelitis*, which is a deep bone infection caused by bacteria entering the bone of an open fracture or after orthopedic surgery. Even less common would be the *neoplastic* diseases, or tumors (cancer) of the bone. Neither osteomyelitis or neoplasms can or should be treated with chiropractic procedures. This doesn't mean you can't treat your cat's subluxations if your cat has these diseases. The best possible scenario is that the vet treats the disease and the chiropractor treats the subluxations. The chiropractor doesn't treat the *disease*, but the *patient who has the disease*.

NEUROLOGICAL DISORDERS AND ASSOCIATED LAMENESS

Lameness associated with neurological disorders in the feline are rare, accounting for only about one percent of the feline population. When they do occur, they are more related to head injuries (due to car accidents and falls) than to brain tumors or congenital defects. Other causes of feline neurological disorders include nutritional deficiencies, adverse drug reactions (toxicities), and *ischemic encephalopathy* (insufficient blood supply to the brain).

The more moderate head injuries present symptoms that are consistent with a *concussion*, such as loss of consciousness, irregular breathing, a staggered gait, and abnormal pupil size. If the brain or spinal cord sustained no structural or tissue damage, the cat's chances of recovery are good. However, any damage done to the central nervous system (brain and spinal cord) is permanent, since those cells do not regenerate. Spinal nerves and other peripheral nerves have some regenerative capabilities, but they still heal very slowly.

By and large, cats displaying neurological conditions due to congenital disorders, and not trauma, are those cats who are actually *bred* to be deformed. The most notable example is the "tail-less" Manx cat. The Manx is predisposed to *spina bifida*, a defective closure of the lower portion the vertebral column, which may encroach spinal nerve roots and the spinal cord. Various types of neurological disorders may result from this including hind limb paralysis, and problems with urinary and defecation control, since the nerves controlling those functions become impaired.

Congenital disorders are not only due to selective breeding. It has been found that medications such as *griseofulvin*, which is used for the treatment of ringworm, can cause birth defects when given to pregnant queens. These defects include spina bifida, cleft palate, and shortened tails and hind limbs.

Infectious diseases, albeit rare, also contribute to the list of neurological disorders that cause physical impairments. Two notable examples of this are *feline infectious peritonitis* and *rabies*. In the former, abdominal cavity tissues are affected, but the nervous system is involved as well. The signs of infectious peritonitis include paralysis of the hind limbs, seizures, head-tilt, and tremors. Rabies is the better known of the two. In this often fatal disease, the cat becomes vicious and, of course, very dangerous. Cats or other animals can transmit rabies by biting and infecting the wound with saliva.

Parasitic diseases, such as *Cuterebra* (fly larvae) and *Dirofilaria immitis* (heartworms), can also cause neurological impairments if they make their way to the brain—but again, these are very rare occurrences.

Nervous system disorders caused by nutritional deficiencies are seen infrequently. A lack of vitamin B_1 (thiamine) can produce degenerative changes of the brain in cats. In these unusual cases, the cat may experience seizures and will tuck its head down and roll itself up into a ball when handled. A thiamine deficiency is largely due to a diet rich in fish such as herring and carp, which contain an enzyme which destroys the vitamin. But if recognized in the early stages, this disorder can be cured by feeding the cat a vitamin-balanced diet.

Degenerative changes such as intervertebral disc disease, as seen in older cats, may cause nerve-related impairments since the affected disc puts pressure on the corresponding spinal nerve. Again, these conditions are rare among cats.

The more serious conditions that can cause neurological impairments include tumors, *feline ischemic encephalopathy* (a stroke-like disease caused by a lack of blood supply to the brain), epilepsy (resulting in seizures), and *feline hyperesthesia syndrome* (a.k.a. rolling-skin syndrome, seen in Siamese cats). The cat suffering from this syndrome will display a number of signs including ripping of the skin (near its back), biting at its tail, frenzied meowing, hallucinations, or just plain acting crazy. This condition, which is most successful if treated with anti-convulsant drugs, is thought to be caused by organic disease. Therefore, a thorough medical screening by a vet will determine if the cat suffers from any internal nutritional deficiencies or infectious diseases.

A more common disorder causing neurological disturbances in cats is *peripheral vestibular dysfunction*, which is attributed to a malady of the nerve that controls the inner part of the ear (the *vestibulocochlear nerve*). Cats afflicted with this disorder demonstrate loss of balance, disorientation, and stumbling, with early signs being vomiting and nausea. The causes for this condition are fractures within the bony frame of the ear (labyrinth), inner ear infections, and tumors of the inner ear.

The above information just gives you a little taste of what types of disorders can cause a cat to appear impaired. Any peculiar movements or behavior by your cat should be taken seriously and brought to the immediate attention of your vet. Most of the chiropractic adjustments presented in this book are safe to use even with the manifestation of these conditions. Nevertheless, you should always use caution and seek professional advice before administering any sort of health care procedure on your cat.

CHAPTER 6

GENERAL EXAMINATION

The purpose of the chiropractic adjustment is to restore normal joint motion to reduce stress on soft tissues, which include muscles, ligaments, tendons, and especially spinal nerves. Therefore, the examination procedures in this chapter are not designed to arrive at medical diagnosis; rather, they yield an educated chiropractic appraisal of joint function based on objective evaluation findings. Once you've made your assessment, you may proceed with the proper adjustments to restore joint function in your cat.

OBSERVATION

Observing your cat in motion will give you a bird's-eye view of possible joint problems. It's only after this evaluation that you should proceed with the hands-on physical examination.

There are very effective techniques to make your cat walk and run for you in ways to properly assess joint motion. There are ways to get your cat moving without looking conspicuous. I'm not suggesting you place a queen in heat in front of a tom. However, a wind-up mechanical mouse or an equivalent will do the job just fine. A remote control toy is ideal since you can regulate the speed and analyze the cat at various levels. When you place this mouse or toy on the floor, make sure your cat is interested. If he refuses to chase the toy in motion, he may be lame altogether—or he may simply think you've flipped your lid. In any case, once he gets going, look for alterations in normal walking and running. If you're really ambitious, you can videotape a series of walking sequences for further study.

What is Normal Walking?

Cats have a definite walking pattern, which is basically diagonal. The step of a forefoot is always followed by that of the diagonally opposite foot. The basic walking pattern is: left hind foot, right forefoot, right hind foot, left forefoot (Fig. 6-1). The forelimbs support over half of the cat's body weight while acting as rudders to guide the cat. The hind limbs are used for propulsion.

Fig. 6-1.
The cat's basic walking pattern is: left hind foot, right forefoot, right hind foot, left forefoot.

What About Running?

Cats are natural born short-distance runners. A domestic cat can attain speeds up to 31 miles per hour (a cheetah can run up to 70 miles per hour). The reason a cat can run fast is that its spine is extremely flexible and it can take long, extended strides. You'll notice while your cat is running fast it almost appears airborne. This is because during top speeds, its limbs become fully extended and all four of them leave the ground. This full limb extension and flight allows the cat to "eat" a generous measure of real estate at once, instead of making multiple ground contacts with its feet. If your cat can run, but can't run fast, check for lower back problems, since the lower back and hind limb muscles are the ones used for propulsion and speed.

Cats Are Good Climbers (Up, That Is!)

If your cat has a difficult time climbing a tree, again check for lower back problems (unless, of course, you had him declawed). The lower back and leg muscles are used to propel the cat up a tree, but aren't very useful for climbing down. While a cat is climbing up, its lower leg muscles support most of its body weight while the claws of the forelegs hook and grip into the tree. But cats often get caught in trees because they can't climb down very well: their claws face the wrong way. Thus, a cat who isn't rescued must climb down backwards using slow and very undignified contortions.

As with climbing, if a cat cannot jump very well, look for lower back or muscle conditions, since the hind limb muscles launch and propel the cat up during jumping.

Twelve Signs of Trouble

Most feline lameness conditions are due to accidents or fights. Some are due to infections, wounds, or (less frequently) metabolic and nutritional disorders (see Chapter 5). The following list will give you a general idea of what to look for during the visual inspection of your cat. For some of these signs, you'll have to feel your cat's limbs. Keep in mind that signs such as swelling, oozing, fractures, flaccidity of a limb, or delirium, to name just a few, are *not* chiropractic cases and should be referred to your vet. Also, if you suspect lameness of a limb, take your cat's temperature before you perform any other exam. A fever of 104° to 105° often signifies an infection or an abscess due to a bite wound.

1. Limping, the most common sign of lameness, is easy to see. There are several possible reasons why a cat drags a leg and cannot put weight on it. If you touch the affected leg and the cat flinches in pain, it might be infected, or the cat might have had an injury. This indicates a problem with the distressed leg, and not a pinched nerve in the spine.

2. If the affected limb (the left foreleg, for example) is thicker than its opposite limb (the right foreleg), this indicates either a fracture or a sprain.

3. Seeing blood is never a good sign. But if the cat doesn't appear to be disabled, it's probably treatable by simple first aid as prescribed by your vet.

4. Swelling of a limb can be just about anything, including tumors. If the swelling doesn't cause lameness, it could be something more serious than an injury, and your cat should be checked.

5. Head bobbing is a sign of a lame front leg. The cat's head will come up as the painful leg touches the ground, thus reducing pressure on the affected leg. The head will bob down when a sore rear leg touches the ground.

6. If your cat bends one limb while standing, that limb is the painful one.

7. A limping cat walks out of sync, "leading" with the painful leg while walking.

8. When the cat stands on all fours, a painful leg's foot appears smaller than the opposite foot, since less pressure is put on the painful one.

9. Again, while your cat is standing on all fours, gently lift each leg up. The foot that comes off the floor most easily is the painful one, because the cat is putting less weight on it, and is in too much pain to resist.

10. A sudden weakness in both hind legs, if each individual limb is otherwise normal, suggests a pinched nerve in the lower spine, or possibly in the neck (see the Short Leg Analysis in Chapter 7).

11. Check the foot pads and claws. Is your cat limping because he has a broken nail or a thorn in his foot? Is there paint or tar on the footpads? If so, these substances can cause sores or abscesses on the foot and between the digits, since the cat will try and chew that stuff away.

12. Excessive cold or hot spots. While hot spots mean swelling (edema), infection or inflammation, cold spots can be something far more serious. A fairly common feline problem that causes hind leg weakness is called *arterial embolism*. Here, a piece of fibrous matter blocks the arteries that supply blood to the hind legs. This may occur suddenly and can occur in cats of all ages. You might think of an arterial thromboembolism as a "stroke" of the hind legs, since stroke-like signs are noticed. These signs include weakness and paralysis of both hind legs, feeling of cold in both legs (since no warm blood is reaching them), and pain. Another sign would be lack of a *femoral pulse*. To check this pulse, lightly place your fingers in the middle of your cat's upper inner thigh, and hold this position for about fifteen seconds while you count the number of beats. Incidentally, the number of pulse beats should equal the number of heartbeats.

CAUSES OF SOME NEUROLOGICAL DISORDERS

Staggering, limping, and paralysis are not always caused by a sore back, injured limbs, or sprained muscles. Sometimes wobbling is due to less obvious causes, such as subtle neurological disorders. Here are just a few causes of nervous disorders:

1. Ingesting poisons. Certain poisons cause paralysis, and other physical signs such as convulsions, coma, and muscle stiffness. The most common types of poisons

that cats ingest include arsenic from horticultural sprays and rat poisons, lead from paint, aspirin from open bottles, and chlorinated hydrocarbons (DDT, Gamma BHC) from insecticides. If you suspect your cat ingested any of the above, call your vet immediately.

2. Paralysis affecting only the hind limbs may indicate spinal cord disease or damage.

3. Middle ear infections can also lead you to believe your cat is lame or has a neurological disorder. The signs include tilting of the head toward the affected side, circling, staggering, loss of balance, and deafness.

A General Musculoskeletal Exam

Before you begin checking for the subtle signs of vertebral subluxations, give your cat the once-over. Make sure that all his joints bend and flex as they should, and that no conspicuous marks are present that would preclude chiropractic adjusting (see Chapter 8, Contraindications).

The Once-Over Procedure

Sit next to your cat on the floor and gently feel the muscles and joints in this order:

1. The head. Feel around the entire head (avoiding the eyes). You will notice several bumpy areas at the top of the skull and at its base. Most of these bumps occur naturally in the skull. It's when you feel differences in the soft tissues from one side to the other that you

should be concerned. Hard or squashy lumps on the head are not normal. Feel behind the ears for any tenderness. If the cat flinches or otherwise warns you to stop, then stop. A tenderness noticed at the base of the skull could denote a subluxation in the upper neck region. Make a note of this point.

2. Check the spine in one sweep. With your thumb and index finger on one hand about an inch apart, feel the first cervical vertebra right below the skull and slowly glide your fingers down the spine with moderate pressure (Fig. 6-2). Write down any signs of pain.

3. Close and open (flex and extend) the joints of the front and back limbs. Is their action smooth, or do

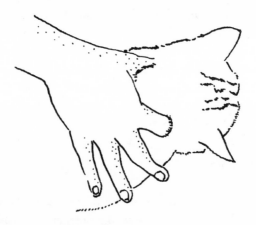

Fig. 6-2.
Palpating the spine, starting with the atlas (first neck bone) and scanning down with your thumb and index finger. You're checking for muscle knots, increased heat, and spinal motion.

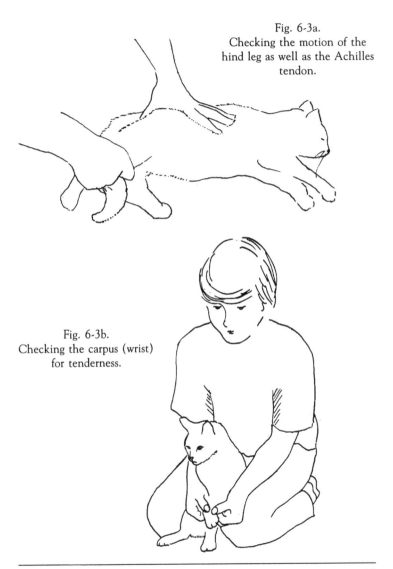

Fig. 6-3a.
Checking the motion of the hind leg as well as the Achilles tendon.

Fig. 6-3b.
Checking the carpus (wrist) for tenderness.

they move like a stuck dresser drawer? While you're feeling the hind limbs, check the Achilles tendon to make sure it is taut (Fig. 6-3). When you check the front limbs, press the carpus (wrist bones) and check for tenderness.

4. Feel the digits (toes) and check for debris. A thorn will cause limping.

5. Feel the hip bones and notice if one side "lumps out" more than the other. Cats involved in accidents can dislocate the thigh bone (the head of the femur) at the hip socket. If this is the case, your cat will cry in pain when you press that spot (Fig. 6-4).

6. Go back to the upper part of the mid-back (shoulder area) and check the scapulas (wings). If one shoulder is higher than the other, press each side and check for tenderness. Remember which side is painful when you do the chiropractic exam.

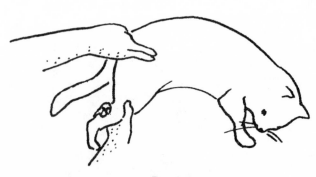

Fig. 6-4.
Feeling the cat's hip socket for lameness.

7. Place your hands under the entire rib cage, feel the chest and wait about a minute so your cat can take several breaths. A badly bruised rib will cause painful breathing, and your cat will sometimes display a faint muscle spasm over the injured rib. If you do notice an injured rib, follow its path to the spine and make a note of the related vertebra. This may be a vertebral subluxation.

8. Check the tail by grasping it and *gently* pulling it from side to side. A lot can be gleaned from a painful tail, especially lower back disorders. Make a note of which side hurt when the tail was pulled. That's often the side of back or hip pain.

9. Lastly, with an open hand, check for areas of excessive heat by slowly waving your hand an inch *over* your cat's spine and rest of the body. Areas of increased heat from inflamed areas can be discovered this way. By placing your hand directly on the body, your own tactile sensations will get in the way of feeling the differences in heat.

CHAPTER 7

THE CHIROPRACTIC EXAMINATION (LOCATING FELINE SUBLUXATIONS)

The next few pages will shed some light on the most frequently asked question about feline chiropractic: "How do I know if my cat is subluxated and needs to be adjusted?"

To answer this question, you must first identify the problem. The feline subluxation isn't always obvious. Where did it come from? How did it get into the country? Should we tell sloppy cats not to litter? We all know what a subluxation is, as described in Chapter 2. The main thing that interests cat owners is how this applies in the real world. "What does it look or feel like on my cat?"

There are three physical properties that you can feel on your cat which identify the vertebral subluxation: abnormally hard muscle spots next to the vertebrae, increased heat over those muscle spots, *and* restricted joint motion associated with those muscle areas. If any of these qualities are missing, it's not a true subluxation, but rather a *compensation*, which is a milder condition cleverly disguised as a subluxation. A compensation is when your mid-back muscles hurt because you had to contort them in such a way to make your ailing lower back feel better. Those aching mid-back muscles would lack one of those three ingredients that make up a true subluxation. Increased heat over the muscle would be the most common quality missing from a compensating muscle, since heat implies inflammation of a nerve. *A true subluxation will always exhibit heat around the nerve.* More specifically, the heat generated from a hard muscle over the vertebrae often radiates from the intervertebral foramen (IVF—see Chapter 3) to let you know the house is on fire.

CHECKING FOR PAIN AND SUBLUXATIONS

The three components of a subluxation examination are *static palpation* (feeling the bones and muscles without moving the joints), *motion palpation* (feeling the muscles and bones by moving the joints), and an *X-ray evaluation* to study spinal distortions. We're only going to concern ourselves with the first two, since X-ray machines are no longer a household item, and because I rarely use radiographs to diagnose subluxations. This is not to say that X-rays aren't useful. They certainly are. But animal X-rays and analysis are strictly a veterinary tool used to diagnose fractures and pathology. I will, however, request an X-ray report from a vet if a broken bone or disease is suspected.

Static Palpation of the Neck

You and your cat should be relaxed and sitting on the floor. A higher surface, like a table, may disconcert the cat and make him feel less secure.

The first bone to examine is the atlas (the first cervical vertebra). Place your thumb and index finger on each side of the atlas (near the base of the skull) (Fig. 7-1). Those bumps you feel on each side are the atlas wings, and as you'll notice are very palpable. Make a mental note of the bigger or harder feeling bump. The bigger side usually indicates the side of the subluxation. Also note if the bigger side feels warmer than the other. Detecting hot or cold spots are all part of static palpation. As a reminder, hot spots indicate tissue inflammation and cold spots denote less blood to the area.

Next, run the same two fingers down each side of the neck until you reach the shoulders and compare the feel of each side. Again, if you notice larger spots (muscle or bone) on one side and not the other, make a note of it.

The bony sides of the neck vertebrae are called the *bodies*.

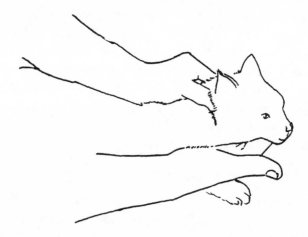

Fig. 7-1.
Determining which atlas wing (bump) feels bigger. The bigger side is usually the side you adjust.

Wherever you feel a side bone stick out more, you're feeling a vertebral body. This, again, is usually the site of the subluxation. A reminder: Except for the second neck bone (axis) and the seventh, most of the "spines" of the cervical vertebra *cannot* be felt (and the atlas doesn't have a spine). Therefore, during static palpation, you will rely mostly on how the cervical bodies feel.

You should be making notes on your findings for every step of the exam. You'll find an examination form at the end of this chapter. Make copies of this form and use it every time you adjust your cat. After a few months, you can review all of your notes, and your cat will have a chiropractic profile.

It's especially important to keep a record on how the unusual muscle spots felt. What was the texture of the muscle? Was it very hard? If so, that could just be a spasm. Was it squashy? That indicates an injury. These notes will come in handy if at-home physical therapy, such as heat and ice, are indicated (see Chapter 16).

Motion Palpation of the Neck

Unless your cat has a *wry-neck*, which is the neck twisted to one side due to obvious unilateral muscle spasms, you're going to have to find the fixed joints yourself. That's what motion palpation determines: where are the stuck joints, or those exhibiting *aberrant motion?* An example of aberrant motion might be a file cabinet drawer that snags when you try to pull it out, but works nonetheless. You can live with the cabinet always getting stuck on something, as long as it keeps working, but you do get annoyed after a while and want it fixed. This is the case with most cervical subluxations. As people, we don't do something about our aberrant motion until something obstructs us from our daily routine.

The first neck joint to be checked is between the atlas (first neck bone) and the base of the skull (occiput). This is known as the "yes" joint, since it allows the cat to move its head up (*neck extension*) and down (*flexion*). Place the tips of your index finger and thumb of one hand behind your cat's neck on this joint and gently lift his chin up with your other hand (Fig. 7-2). Note whether the cat veers his nose more to one side after three attempts. If, for example, the cat naturally

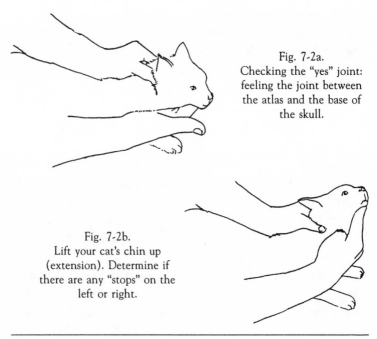

Fig. 7-2a.
Checking the "yes" joint: feeling the joint between the atlas and the base of the skull.

Fig. 7-2b.
Lift your cat's chin up (extension). Determine if there are any "stops" on the left or right.

wants to move his head to the right during the "yes" check, then look for a fixed atlas on the right. This will be the site of the thrust (impulse) when you go to adjust.

Next, check the motion between the atlas and the second neck bone (axis). This is known as the "no" joint, and allows the cat to rotate his head. Again, place the same two fingers behind the cat's neck (this time feeling the axis), then rotate his nose up to one side, return to center, then up towards the other side (Fig. 7-3). Since this space is so small, your thumb

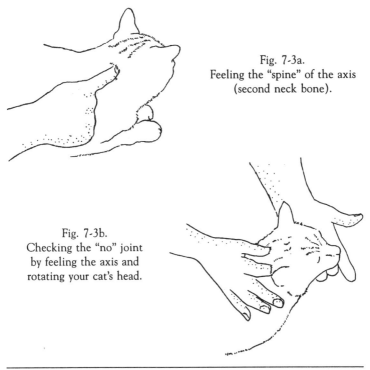

Fig. 7-3a.
Feeling the "spine" of the axis (second neck bone).

Fig. 7-3b.
Checking the "no" joint by feeling the axis and rotating your cat's head.

and index finger will almost be touching each other ("pinching" the spine of the axis) while checking this joint. As an illustration, let's say your cat had less left rotation. You would take this information, coupled with your static palpation findings (a hard muscle knot on the left side of the axis, for example), then choose the appropriate adjustment from the list of neck methods (Chapter 12). You would either do a manipulative move or simply press your finger into the hard muscle, as done in pressure point techniques.

The remainder of the neck bones are very easy to test because you're checking one basic motion, lateral flexion. Simply place your index finger to the side of your cat's neck and bend his neck over your finger. Note the "stops" on either side (Fig. 7-4).

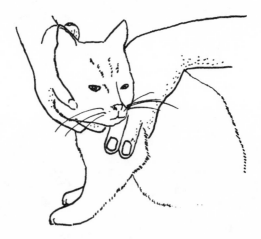

Fig. 7-4.
Gently bend your cat's neck over your index finger, checking for "stops" along the way.

Lastly, if you think the cat is hurting more on one side, conduct this little traction test. Place your thumb and index finger under the base of the skull and gently pull the head up (Fig. 7-5). If your cat has neck pain and muscle spasms, he'll bend his neck towards the painful side.

Static Palpation of the Mid-Back

This heading is somewhat of a contradiction. A cat's mid-back is so flexible that it's almost impossible to conduct a static palpation examination without moving the spine. Conversely, if a cat does have a pinched nerve in the mid-back (thoracics/dorsal vertebrae), it will be easy to spot. A cat depends on a flexible mid-back to run, leap, and especially show fear in the

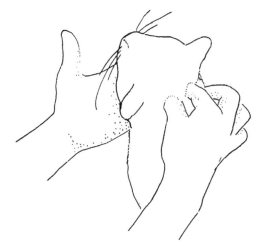

Fig. 7-5.
Gently traction your cat's head forward. During this test, he will bend his head toward the painful side.

defensive "arched back" pose. Cats that cannot arch their backs are in pain.

Whenever you examine your cat's mid- or lower back, you should do this with one hand on your cat's back and the other hand supporting him under the chest or abdomen. The supporting hand, in essence, acts as the chiropractic table.

To palpate your cat's thoracics, simply place the tip of your thumb and index finger on each side of the first dorsal "spine," and in one slow continuous pass, scan down the back till you reach the last rib (Fig. 7-6). Make a note of the "speed bumps"

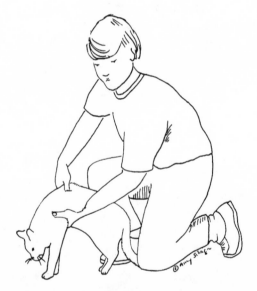

Fig. 7-6.
Feeling the mid-back for muscle spasms and decreased spinal motion.
Note: It helps to lift the chest up a bit. This will lower the scapular (shoulder) bones and help you feel the upper thoracics better.

along the way, which are either ribs or hard muscle knots. Next, go back to the top of the thoracics and individually press into each of these bumps until you've tested all of them. Ask yourself the usual questions. Did your cat flinch when you pressed any of these spots? Was that spot hotter or colder than the other spots? A rib bump should not be hotter than the rest of the spine, but a hard muscle might be. If so, this is most likely one of the subluxations.

Motion Palpation of the Mid-Back

This is easy as well. Support your cat with one hand under his chest, place the tip of your thumb and index finger on the first thoracic, and push down. Do this for each mid-back bone, with an up-down rhythm on each joint, until you've reached the last rib and note which joint was fixed. I'm jumping ahead here, but I often adjust those fixed mid-back joints as soon as I find them by impulsing down a little harder on the second pass.

Static Palpation of the Lower Back

These bones and joints (lumbars) feel about the same as the thoracics, only without the ribs. The real difference is with motion palpation.

Motion Palpation of the Lower Back

Unlike people, cats have no "small" of their back—that is, no curve that makes their lumbars dip down (see Fig. 3-7). Their lumbar curve is an extension of the thoracic curve. However, the lumbars, along with the sacrum (the bone below the last lumbar), have everything to do with how the hips move. Therefore, if your cat has lower back pain, it could be emanating from the hips, lumbars, or hind legs. Disc problems, while uncommon, are seen more in the lumbars than in the thoracics. A badly herniated disc in the lower spine will cause muscle spasms anywhere in the lumbars. When you push down on a low-back joint during motion palpation, your cat would cry out in pain if he had a slipped disc.

The transition areas of the spine are often the sites of subluxations, since these are the areas of greatest movement. A transition area is where one section of the spine ends and another begins (e.g., between the last thoracic and the first lumbar).

Static Palpation of the Hips and Sacrum

You will recall from the anatomy discussion in Chapter 3 that most of the sacrum cannot be felt, since it is wedged too deeply between the two pelvic bones. If you try to feel the bone below the last lumbar, which is the sacrum, you'll just feel a space and simply know the sacrum is there below your finger. What can be felt is the motion of the sacro-iliac joint. This is where the hips meet the sacrum (Fig. 7-7). To feel the sacro-iliac joint, you first have to feel for the top of each hip bone. These tops are called the *posterior-superior-iliac spines* (PSIS) or *Tuber Sacrale* (see Fig. 3-19). The sacrum lies between these two points.

Motion Palpation of the Hips

To feel for a fixed hip joint, place your cat on one side. Feel the top of the hip bone (PSIS) with one hand, and with your other hand, grasp the thigh bone (femur) and extend the leg backwards (Fig. 7-8). Then turn your cat over and repeat. Ask yourself which leg moved back easier. Did one hip seem to glide more effortlessly than the other? If so, was it because your cat injured that leg or hip socket? Make sure you check the hip

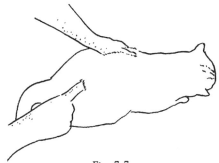

Fig. 7-7.
The sacrum, the bone directly below the last lumbar, is not always palpable, but the space it occupies can be felt just above the root of the tail.

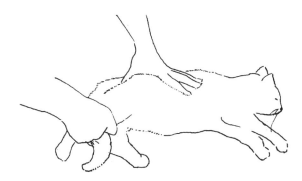

Fig. 7-8.
Feeling for a fixed hip joint. This check tests the motion of the sacro-iliac joint. Compare this to checking the "ball-and-socket" joint (Fig. 6-4).

socket (*acetabulum*). Put your fingers on the socket and again extend your cat's leg backward. If you noticed a "pop" during this, your cat may have had a falling accident. Cats, unlike dogs, do not suffer from hip dysplasia, but they can have injuries resembling hip dysplasia.

OTHER JOINT TESTS

1. **Foreleg tests.** First, feel each foreleg and check for swelling, debris, and tender areas. Next, flex (bend) the foreleg joints, including the elbow, and check for stiffness. If you suspect your cat has a weak or painful front leg and want to find out which one, do the *wheelbarrow test* (Fig. 7-9). To do this, lift your cat's hind legs off the ground while he does a handstand.

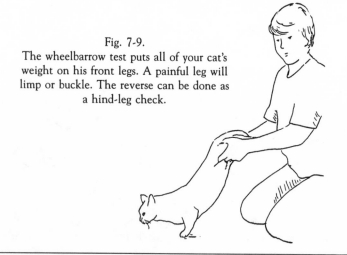

Fig. 7-9.
The wheelbarrow test puts all of your cat's weight on his front legs. A painful leg will limp or buckle. The reverse can be done as a hind-leg check.

Walk him around, backwards and forwards, to see if one of these limbs teeters, indicating that he can't support his weight with that limb. After this, feel the carpus (wrist bones) by moving the wrist up and down. Then feel the toes, and again, check for debris. Apply a little pressure to each digit. Your cat should not flinch with mild pressure.

2. **Hind leg tests.** As with the foreleg tests, test the joints by flexing the leg. The wheelbarrow test can be done here in reverse to check for hind leg weakness. Check the toes and the foot pads just as you did the front ones. Also, check the Achilles tendon for tender spots by lightly squeezing it. Feel the stifle (knee) and the hock for stiffness. Cats have tarsal bones which compose the hock, but these are not flexible like the front leg carpus. So don't look to do a "wrist" adjustment on a hind leg. Remember, the hock is the equivalent of our heel bone, thus, cats walk on their toes while their heel is sticking up.

SHORT~LEG ANALYSIS

The short-leg analysis is a standard test taught in all chiropractic colleges for the purpose of finding subluxations of the neck, lower back and hip. This routine evaluation helps solidify your earlier examination findings.

A leg that appears to be short does not mean the actual leg bone is short, but that a muscular imbalance is present, coupled with a vertebral or hip misalignment. To perform this test, situate yourself behind the standing cat and lift his hind legs up and backwards so he is now standing on just his front legs (Fig. 7-10). When lifting the hind legs, make sure you grasp the legs high on the thighs, close to the abdomen. Now compare the feet. Notice if one leg wants to reflexively pull away from you, or if one leg appears to be shorter than the other. Next, apply

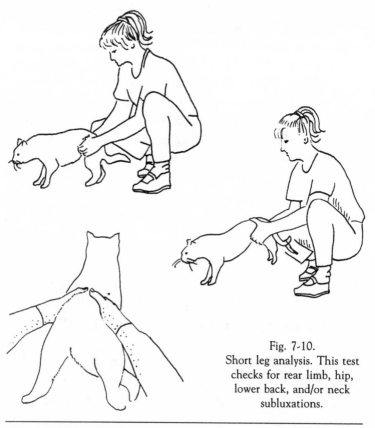

Fig. 7-10.
Short leg analysis. This test checks for rear limb, hip, lower back, and/or neck subluxations.

a quick "punch" with your fingers into the rump muscles of the short-leg side (the "punch" should be as hard as thumping a watermelon). If the short leg temporarily lengthens and evens out with the other, then your cat may have a low-back or hip subluxation on the side of the short leg.

You may also check for neck subluxations during the short-leg analysis. While the cat's legs are extended, as in the example above, have an assistant gently turn the cat's neck to the same side as the short leg. (The cat's nose will then be pointing toward the short-leg side). A short leg that lengthens during this maneuver indicates a neck subluxation on that side. For example, a short right leg that lengthens when the cat turns his head to the right would indicate a subluxation somewhere on the right side of the neck.

EXAMINATION FORM

Cat's Name _____

Owner _____

Date _____

LEGEND:
MK=Muscle Knot
HS=Hot Spot
FJ=Fixed Joint
C=Compensation Area
P=Pain
S=Subluxation

Note: You may use
none or all of the
abbreviations for any
vertebral area. Just
write them next to the
specified bone.

LEFT _____C1_____ RIGHT

_____C2_____

_____C3_____

_____C4_____

_____C5_____

_____C6_____

_____C7_____

_____T1_____

_____T2_____

_____T3_____

_____T4_____

_____T5_____

_____T6_____

_____T7_____

_____T8_____

_____T9_____

_____T10_____

_____T11_____

_____T12_____

_____T13_____

_____L1_____

_____L2_____

_____L3_____

_____L4_____

_____L5_____

_____L6_____

_____L7_____

_____ LEFT HIP   RIGHT HIP_____

_____S1_____

_____S2_____

_____S3_____

_____TAIL_____

CHAPTER 8

CONTRAINDICATIONS

Contraindications are reasons why you shouldn't use chiropractic manipulation on your cat. This refers to those methods that require thrusting into a joint or the use of traction. Soft tissue methods, such as the Ligament Push (Logan Basic Technique; see Chapter 15) or trigger point techniques, are safe to do under most circumstances. The primary contraindication is utilizing chiropractic methods for conditions that generally don't respond to this treatment, and delaying the use of appropriate therapies. This is why your cat should be thoroughly checked by a veterinarian before administering any chiropractic procedures.

Since most of the following contraindications are just common sense, they are the same ones listed in *The Well Adjusted Dog,* with some modifications.

1. **Fractures.** Never adjust a bone that has an unhealed fracture, or a bone near such a fracture.
2. **Recent trauma.** This is always a problem with cats, and they're so flexible, it's sometimes hard to tell if they were injured. Nevertheless, if you suspect your cat has had a fall, don't adjust her.
3. **Emotional stress.** A cat who is emotionally charged

(like after a confrontation with a dog) is a bundle of nerves, and his whole body will feel subluxated. Wait an hour or two after the incident before adjusting.

4. **Vascular conditions (Rare).** Only a veterinarian can determine this. A buildup of plaque in the vertebral arteries would contraindicate spinal manipulation, especially of the neck.

5. **Tumors.** The possibility of causing a fracture by rendering an adjustment is increased in the cancer patient, especially if the bone itself is malignant.

6. **Bone infections.** While these are rare, they still exist and should be ruled out by a veterinary medical examination. Some signs of bone infections are tissue atrophy, increased warmth, and *edema* (swelling due to fluid buildup). Sometimes a soft-tissue mass will be present that lacks roundness and will change shape under pressure.

7. **Nerve damage.** The sensation over these areas is usually decreased; therefore, the degree of susceptibility to injury cannot be adequately assessed.

8. **Old surgical scars**, especially on or near a joint. These are signs that the cat has had something wrong with it. Find out what it was before you adjust.

9. **Profuse joint swelling.** Large areas of increased heat and excess fluid are signs of a serious medical condition.

10. **Arthritis**. This is less common with cats than dogs, and the contraindication refers only to severe cases. Arthritic cats cannot be easily adjusted, and the prac-

titioner may be tempted to use unacceptable force to perform the adjustment. Use soft-tissue methods instead.

11. **Skin lesions.** Adjusting over a lesion can aggravate the site and cause infections.

12. **Prostheses.** I've only seen one case where a cat had part of an artificial leg (hip joint). Though prosthetics are seen more commonly with dysplastic dogs, you may have a cat who had a limb replaced. Use caution here. You can still do a vertebral adjustment, just be extra careful during the stabilization phase of the procedure. A cat with a prosthesis can't effectively support itself during a "standing" procedure. This often depends on the effectiveness of the replacement limb.

14. **Medications.** Pain killers and anti-inflammatory drugs, such as phenylbutazone, can often mask symptoms—even though chiropractic care may help reduce the need for such medications. Side effects of medications (as well as some food supplements) may present themselves as subluxation, i.e., increased or decreased muscle tone over the spine (see Chapter 2 on poisons).

15. **Herniated, or "slipped," disc.** Do not adjust at the site of the herniation; rather, work on the surrounding subluxations.

Chapter 9

Handling and Safety

There are correct ways to pick up your cat when you hold or play with him. However, these next few pages are not about that, but rather, how to keep you and your cat safe during the adjustment. **Note:** Whenever you adjust your cat, he should always be situated on a table or the floor. There is never an instance where your cat will be adjusted unsupported.

Cat Hazards

Claws! Claws! Claws! Did you ever wonder why your cat never pressured you to buy him a pocket knife? That's because he has ten sharp swords on his front paws at his disposal, and yours! Unless your cat has been declawed (which, in my opinion, is mutilation), then you need to protect yourself during those chiropractic procedures, which requires more finesse. One way to safeguard yourself from the claws is to roll your cat in a large towel or small blanket, keeping his head exposed (Fig. 9-1). However, this is only useful if you're adjusting his neck. As you can see, once you roll up your cat, you lose access to the rest of his body. If you don't want to use the towel method, you may fit a protective bootie over each paw, including the back ones. This will allow you to work on his entire spine.

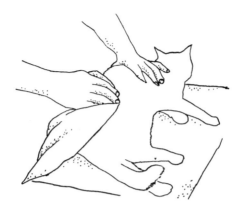

Fig. 9-1a.
Rolling your cat up in a large towel or blanket will safeguard you from his claws during a neck adjustment.

Fig. 9-1b.
Make sure your cat's head and neck are exposed.

What About Biting?

People frequently ask me if I've ever been hurt while adjusting. I can't even count the number of times I've been bitten, scratched, or stepped on—even by animal patients!

Indeed, biting can be a problem. Cats have very sharp teeth. This danger is much more prevalent with canine adjusting, but dogs can be muzzled. There are only a few methods that require you to grasp the cat's face, as in some of the neck techniques. You can shield your hand from the cat's mouth by placing a barrier, such as a piece of cloth, over the cat's face (Fig. 9-2). He won't like this, but the adjustment just takes a few seconds. Just make sure you don't interrupt his breathing.

What About Wearing Gloves?

Gloves hinder your tactile sensations. You won't be able to feel anything, so don't use them. The only time I use latex gloves (for sanitary reasons) is when I administer the Ligament Push (Logan Basic Technique; see Chapter 15), since the contact is near the anus. Latex gloves, however, will not protect you from bites or scratches.

NICE KITTY!

In my first animal chiropractic book, *The Well Adjusted Dog*, I included a section on the biting and least biting breeds. The question of which cat is most likely to "attack" you seems to be more subjective than with dogs. I personally think there's no such thing as a bad cat—only people who treat cats badly. A

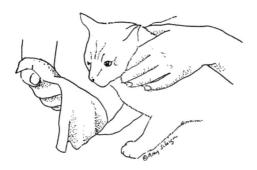

Fig. 9-2a.
Covering your cat's face with a piece of cloth protects you against biting.

Fig. 9-2b.
His face is covered for only a few seconds during the adjustment.

seemingly aggressive house cat is merely instinctively defending itself from the offender, whether a person or another animal. If you were touched in a sensitive spot, you would jump too!

So again, for what it's worth, here's a list of "affectionate cats" as oppose to the ones that would rather not be handled. You'll notice that the even-tempered, good-natured cats far outweigh the more "frisky" ones. (Source: *You & Your Cat,* by David Taylor; Alfred A. Knopf, 1986).

Affectionate and Good-Natured Breeds

1. Persians (most of them)
2. Birman
3. Ragdoll (has a high pain tolerance, and injuries sometimes go unnoticed)
4. Balinese
5. Turkish Angora
6. British Turkish cat (even likes water!)
7. Maine Coon (but not suited for apartment living)
8. British Shorthairs (all of them)
9. Manx (very odd; no—or minute—tail, and hops like a bunny!)
10. American Shorthair (most of them)
11. American Wirehair
12. Exotic Shorthair
13. Russian Blue
14. Korat
15. Burmese
16. Havana

17. Japanese Bobtail
18. Singapura (if treated right)
19. Tonkinese (actually too friendly for its own good—loves people and cars, which poses a danger)
20. Bombay
21. Snowshoe
22. Rex (friendly and wags its tail like a dog, thus the nickname "poodle cat.")
23. Egyptian Mau

"Friskier" Cats

1. Sphynx (absolutely deserves to be first on this list: hairless, therefore sensitive; they hate to be handled—but who can blame them?)
2. Himalayan (devoted to its owner—not to strangers)
3. Chestnut Brown and Lavender Kashmirs (more inquisitive and enterprising)
4. Siamese and Colorpoint Shorthairs (extroverted, demanding, and jealous, but mostly affectionate cats)
5. Abyssinian and Somali (become restless when confined)
6. Oriental Shorthairs (energetic and inquisitive)

Chapter 10

Adjusting Skills

Here lies the controversy: How much skill is required to deliver a safe, effective chiropractic adjustment? This boils down to who should be doing the adjusting, which is precisely the point of writing a mostly "laymen's" version of animal chiropractic methods.

A chiropractor goes to college for a minimum of six years to become a licensed chiropractic physician. During this period, he or she becomes skilled enough to conduct a clinical practice. So why don't we leave animal adjusting to the competent professional who worked so long and hard to deliver a proficient adjustment? *That's what I'd like to know!!* (See Chapter 1: The Outlaw Doc.) In the meantime, it is up to cat owners to apply safe feline chiropractic methods that don't require a fifth-degree black belt.

Since adjusting skills haven't changed much since the writing of *The Well Adjusted Dog,* the following is a repeat of the chapter bearing the same heading (with slight modifications). The only other difference is the information on the metal mallet; an adjusting instrument you can use in place of the manual thrust.

Just as a pianist has to know how hard to press the key to create the right sound, the feline adjuster should develop certain sensitivities in their hands. There are two physical requirements for administering an adjustment: manual dexterity and muscular coordination.

Manual Dexterity

Traditional chiropractic moves rely on the mind and hand acting as one without hesitation. The type of movement your hands have to make during the adjustment is akin to your wrist action when cracking a whip, or to *Peanuts'* Linus "nailing" a fly out of the air with one quick snap of his blanket. It's speed, not force, that gets the job done safely. This is why an average-sized person is able to adjust a horse—*without* the use of large hammers!

Because the reader of this book won't be doing a lot of "cracking" moves, he or she should focus on developing a keen sense of touch and tactile depth perception. You should be sensitive to the subtle differences in muscle textures and heat variations. Most of the adjusting methods in this book involve applying light pressure, without having to actually deliver a thrust into a bone or joint. The following exercises will help improve your finger and hand skills.

1. **Palpation exercise.** This will help to develop your sense of touch. Place a hair under a piece of notebook paper and see if you can feel the hair underneath. Then put the hair under two pieces of paper, and so on, until you're no longer able to feel the hair. If you can still feel the hair underneath five sheets of paper,

you're above average.

2. **Testing finger depth perception.** Take a two-inch-thick piece of Styrofoam, hold it down with one hand for stabilization, and place your other thumb on the Styrofoam's surface, keeping your wrist straight. This will be your adjusting hand. Situate yourself above the Styrofoam with the elbow of your adjusting arm slightly bent. Now deliver a sudden impulse into the Styrofoam. Your thumb should not make a dent deeper than a quarter of an inch, even with a full and sudden thrust.

3. **Finger dexterity test.** With the palm of your hand on a table and your fingers slightly spread, place a quarter underneath the tip of your pinky. Then, without moving your pinky, slide your ring finger next to your pinky and pull the coin away, positioning it under your ring finger. Repeat this procedure for all your fingers, including your thumb. Then reverse the direction of the fingers. Do this until you can pass the coin from one side of your hand to the next in about five seconds.

Muscular Coordination

At the time of the thrust, your muscles must move in a clean, flawless motion. Your goal is to achieve bull's-eye accuracy. Here are some exercises to improve muscular coordination:

1. Practice driving a two-inch screw into a piece of wood without having to reinsert the screwdriver head.
2. Have someone throw three balls at you, one at a time

in rapid succession. Catch and drop each ball with the same hand.

3. Toss two coins in the air and, with two separate grabs, catch them both.

General Advice

1. Never push into your cat's mid-back without supporting his belly or chest area with your other hand. A human who gets adjusted can lie on his belly, because his rib cage can absorb a light to moderate thrust coming from the back. A cat, however, has a much more vulnerable rib cage configuration and cannot absorb a downward thrust if he lies sprawled out on his belly.

2. For thrusting moves that deliver a sudden impulse into a joint, the force behind the thrust originates from the contraction of your triceps and pectorals (Fig. 10-1).

3. For a "Set and Hold" adjustment, your hands remain at the end of the thrusting position for a few moments to prevent a recoil of the vertebra. This only applies after you've delivered a sudden impulse into a joint.

4. You do not always hear an audible sound or "pop" during the adjustment. Sometimes you will simply feel the vertebrae slide into place.

5. If you want to adjust just one bone, you must contact only that bone. Contacting two bones divides the energy of your thrust in half.

6. The adjusting thrust is a high-velocity, low-amplitude (force) maneuver.

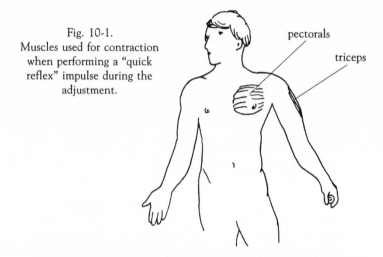

Fig. 10-1.
Muscles used for contraction when performing a "quick reflex" impulse during the adjustment.

pectorals

triceps

7. When pushing into a "spine," joint, or muscle, never push so hard that your cat screams. The phrase "No pain, no gain" does not apply here.
8. Do not apply heat to your cat before the treatment. If your cat is in pain, he may have an inflamed joint or joint swelling that will become worse under heat.
9. Cut your nails.
10. Be wary of your cat's nails (but for heaven's sake, avoid having your cat declawed).

THE METAL MALLET (ACTIVATOR)

The metal mallet (see Fig. 4-1) is a safe, easy-to-operate chiropractic adjusting instrument that can be used in place of most manual adjusting procedures.

Dr. Bill Inman, a respected and very knowledgeable veterinarian from Seattle, Washington, uses the metal mallet exclusively in his practice. His technique, Veterinary Orthopedic Manipulation (V.O.M.™), which utilizes this instrument, is widely accepted by doctors throughout this country and abroad. Together, Dr. Inman and I teach a nationwide animal chiropractic seminar to chiropractors and veterinarians, as well as pet owners. Dr. Inman's seminar materials include the following information about the metal mallet:

1. The device is a spinal accelerometer. Its "firing" creates a fast and concise spinal thrust to the compromised spinal segment.
2. Its action occurs within 2–4 milliseconds.
3. Its thrust at that speed, by Newton's second law of motion, creates a huge force using a very small mass.
4. The very small mass affords an adjustment that cannot torque, twist or harm the tissue, which can occur with a slower manual adjustment using the mass of the practitioner.
5. The quickest manual adjustment possible by a human is 80 milliseconds. The body's reflexive response or resistance is 20 milliseconds. Thus the manual practitioner may well be *4 times too slow* for a resistive pet.
6. With the metal mallet, even resistant, recalcitrant, tense, and non-cooperative pets can be adjusted whether they want to or not.
7. Posture and proper pet positioning is not an issue in metal-mallet-based adjustment.

Assuming that all of the above is true (which it is), why would anyone want to perform a manual adjustment? The answer is that the metal mallet does have its limitations. For example, it cannot adequately free up the joints, especially those of the hips and neck. While this device can be used for extremity adjusting (arms and legs), most traditional chiropractors prefer manual adjusting for these areas. Also, by using regular manipulative methods, you are able to employ traction, which greatly enhances the mobility of a joint. Still, I would recommend using the metal mallet as a means of delivering an adequate adjustment. Naturally, I would recommend the methods contained in this book as being equally safe and effective. (Note that some of the methods are labeled for professional use only.)

About Using the Metal Mallet

You can buy a metal mallet (see ordering instructions near the back of this book), but many of your neighborhood chiropractors already have one. If you are able to borrow one for the day, here are some tips on its use.

1. The intensity of the stroke or impulse can be increased or decreased by adjusting the collar (Fig. 10-2). By turning the collar up towards the tip, which exposes more "rings" below the collar, you are *increasing* the intensity. Conversely, by turning the collar down towards the handle, you are *decreasing* the intensity.
2. For most cat adjusting, expose only one or two rings below the collar.

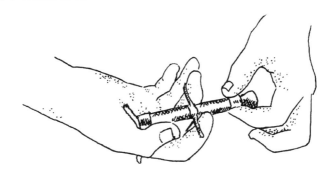

Fig. 10-2.
By turning the metal mallet's collar, you can regulate
the intensity of the impulse.

3. Some models contain a double compression spring at
the handle end. Gross adjustment of stroke intensity
may be made by removing the inner spring, then re-
placing the single spring and finally placing the cap at
the handle end as before (screw handle back on). This
will dramatically reduce stroke intensity.

4. To "fire" the mallet, place your palm on the lower
handle, your index and middle fingers on the middle
hand, and squeeze (Fig. 10-3).

5. Most mallets do not require lubrication. So if you borrow one, don't oil it up.

6. When applying the tip of the mallet to your cat, don't
"dig" it into the skin. A light but sure contact is all
that's necessary.

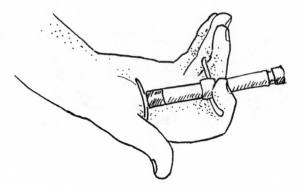

Fig. 10-3.
The impulse/thrust is delivered by squeezing the mallet's handle.

Chapter 11
About the Methods

The feline chiropractic methods, as explained in the next few chapters, were devised to help you restore normal nerve expression in your cat, particularly around the spinal column. This goal can only be accomplished if you feel comfortable administering the procedures. In view of this, I have broken down each method section (neck, mid-back, lower back, etc.) into categories according to the various degrees of difficulty. However, I try to maintain a certain level of impartiality in terms of effectiveness. There are techniques that I prefer over others, but your tastes may differ from mine, especially since you know your cat better than I do. The use of one technique over another often depends on the cat's temperament and his (and your) ability to hold still.

Soft tissue techniques are considered easier than regular joint manipulation moves, but they can be equally effective. There are times when light touch moves are the only ones you should use, since joint manipulation would be considered too harsh on some cats (see Chapter 8: Contraindications).

What Can I Expect After A Treatment?

This is the $64,000 question. Before I answer it, you must remember that there is more than one way to adjust a cat. If any one type of health-care was a cure-all, that's all that would exist. The best any one method can do for your cat is safely reduce spinal nerve pressure. Don't expect a cure for a particular illness, even though you might get one anyway. Also, don't try every single method if your cat doesn't immediately jump up, or fails to land the Friskies commercial. Healing takes time. On the brighter side, when good results do occur, you will often notice them within one to four days.

As important as it is to find subluxations, it is equally important to conduct a post-adjustment exam, which is very similar to the first evaluation. Immediately after the adjustment, motion out and feel the treated area for changes. Are the harder muscles softer? Is there less heat over the suspected subluxated areas? And most importantly, was normal joint motion restored? Then, wait a couple of hours before checking your cat again.

For those of you who are truly beginners, I suggest you start with the soft tissue moves, which are clearly labeled **ST**. These will be the first moves presented for each area of the body. The more involved joint manipulative moves, marked **JM,** require much more practice. A third type of move, utilizing the metal mallet (or activator; see Chapter 10), is a cross between soft tissue techniques and joint manipulation. These are considered as safe as soft tissue moves and will be marked **MM**.

All the methods presented here have been time-tested by some of the best animal chiropractors in the world. But they are still only as good as the current practitioner. The developer of chiropractic, B.J. Palmer, once said, "It's not the *tic*, it's the *tor*." This meant that if the patient didn't get well after the treatment, it wasn't the fault of chiroprac*tic*, but rather, the chiroprac*tor*.

CHAPTER 12

METHODS TO HELP
YOUR CAT'S NECK

These are the chiropractic methods that will help reduce feline subluxations and restore normal joint function to your cat's neck. Use these methods sparingly so as not to stress your cat's joints. Again, you don't always get immediate results. If you feel you've correctly performed the method, wait a day or so and see how your cat responds.

Just for review, here is a quick reference legend of abbreviations and terms used to describe the methods:

1. **ST**—Soft Tissue methods. They are considered safe and easy to do.
2. **JM**—Joint Manipulation. These methods require more practice and should be administered by a professional chiropractor, veterinarian, or a well-trained animal handler.
3. **MM**—Metal Mallet. This is sort of in between the soft tissue and joint manipulation methods. As you recall, the small metal mallet emits a high-amplitude/low-force impulse at the tip. This force is so light that most chiropractors think of the metal mallet methods as soft

tissue techniques. If you decide to use this technique, make sure you follow the manufacturer's safety guidelines. Information on how to order a metal mallet can be found on page 223 of this book.

METHOD ONE: Atlas Release (ST). This easy-to-apply technique helps rid your cat of neck pain, and aids communication between the brain and the body by releasing the muscle spasm barrier between them.

First, feel both atlas wings and notice which "bump" feels bigger (Fig. 12-1). The bigger side usually indicates tighter spastic muscles and pain. To verify a left atlas subluxation, for example, lift your cat's chin up with one finger and feel both atlas wings with the thumb and index finger of your other hand (Fig. 12-2). If you cat's head naturally gravitates more to the left, then that's the side to adjust. To treat, simply place the tip

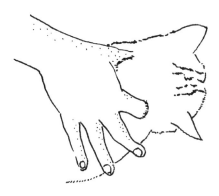

Fig. 12-1.
Determining which atlas wing feels bigger.

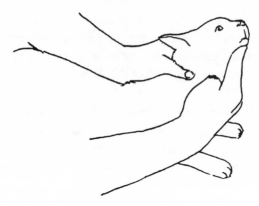

Fig. 12-2.
Feeling both atlas wings while pushing your cat's chin up. Repeat this three times: once pushing the chin straight up, once up and to the right, and lastly, up and to the left. Notice which side feels "stuck."

Fig. 12-3.
Presing your finger into the larger-feeling atlas wing. This helps relieve muscle tension at the base of the skull.

of your thumb or index finger on the bigger bump (in this case, the left atlas wing) and gently, but steadily press towards the opposite side and hold for a full minute (Fig. 12-3). If your cat experiences any discomfort during this procedure, stop or re-duce your pressure. After you've finished, repeat the chin lift exam to see if the fixed atlas has been improved. You may apply this method every other day if necessary.

METHOD TWO: Atlas Extension (ST). If your cat fights you a little during the chin lift exam, he may be experiencing muscle tension between the base of the skull (occiput) and the atlas (the "yes" joint—see Chapter 7). If this is the case, here's the treatment. As in Method One, place your thumb and index finger on each atlas wing with a moderate to firm contact (Fig. 12-4). Next, slowly pinch these two fingers together until they

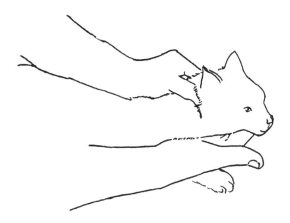

Fig. 12-4.
Contacting both atlas wings with moderate to firm pressure.

meet at the center beneath the skull. This opens up the joint. Retain this pinched position while your other hand gradually lifts the chin up, so your cat's head is fully extended (Fig. 12-5). Hold this position as long as possible. Some cats will only stand for this a few seconds, others for a minute. When you're done, recheck the "Yes" joint.

METHOD THREE: Atlas Traction (ST). This method can be used in place of Method Two and is more of a traction move. If your cat has poor neck extension, as in Method Two, then use this method. **Note:** Use either Method Two **or** Method Three, but not both within a 24-hour period. To apply atlas

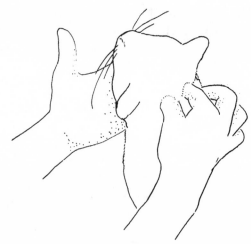

Fig. 12-5.
While retaining the pressure on the atlas wings (Fig. 12-4), pinch your thumb and index finger so they meet at the center beneath the skull. Then lift your cat's chin up. This opens up the joint space.

traction, place your thumb and index finger of one hand underneath each atlas wing. Your other hand is holding your cat still at the shoulders (Fig. 12-6). Next, apply moderate but steady pressure up towards the head and hold for about 30 seconds, then release.

METHOD FOUR: Atlas Toggle (JM/MM). Normally, there would be no question that the atlas toggle would be considered joint manipulation. I refer to this method as being joint manipulation only because it requires an "impulse" which is a minor thrust or quick punch and is necessary to complete the adjustment (Fig. 12-7). This would be the setup for a human toggle. As you can see, the heel of the practitioner's hand contacts one atlas wing (the bigger bump) while the patient lies on his or her side. Then, a quick thrust is applied to that wing to put the atlas in motion. If you recall from Chapter 2,

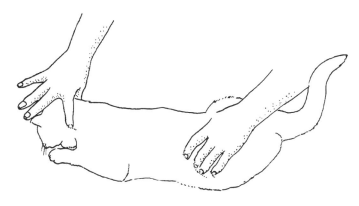

Fig. 12-6.
Applying traction to the atlas.

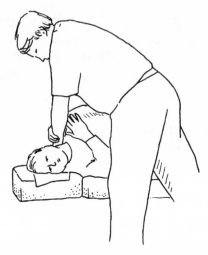

Fig. 12-7a.
Set-up fpr the toggle-recoil adjustment.

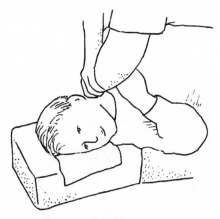

Fig. 12-7b.
The heel of the practitioner's hand contacts the "bigger" atlas wing.

the atlas is a ring-shaped vertebra which is different from all the others. The atlas has a less restrictive joint configuration than the other vertebrae and has the ability to oscillate within its own space when set in motion. Chiropractors often refer to this phenomenon of the atlas as "finding its own level." Its own level means the intended "slots," or where the atlas should be when it's not subluxated.

Before I describe the adjustment, it is worthy of note that the atlas toggle is often referred to as the *toggle recoil* because as soon as you emit the impulse, your hand immediately comes off the contact (bone). This action allows for the oscillation. Compare this to a "set-and-hold" adjustment, where your hands stay at the point of contact for a few seconds after the thrust to *prevent* recoil. The recoil is the action of the elastic muscles snapping back at you once you've let go of it, like a slingshot.

There are two ways to administer the atlas toggle. The first method is to contact the larger wing with the thumb of one hand and stabilize the opposite side of the cat's head with your other hand. Make sure your stabilization hand is not pressing against the "small wing"—if it is, you will be impulsing into "granite" and the atlas will not oscillate. Therefore, stabilize the opposite side above the small wing (occiput, or the side of the head) and the vertebra below, which is the axis (Fig. 12-8) and not the opposite wing. Next, while keeping your contact hand (thumb) and wrist straight and sturdy, deliver a sudden but non-forceful punch into the wing and quickly release. The speed of this impulse is the important component of the adjustment and can be compared to the action of the pricing punch used in grocery stores.

The second way to deliver the atlas toggle is to simply apply the tip of the metal mallet on the large wing (with two rings showing below the collar of the mallet, which will produce a low force) and squeeze the handle (Fig. 12-9). As in the first toggle method, all of the stabilization procedures apply. The beauty of using the metal mallet is that it is already a fast

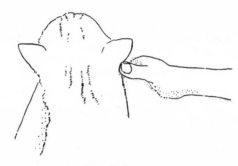

Fig. 12-8.
For a manual toggle adjustment, apply thumb pressure into the atlas wing while stabilizing the opposite side.

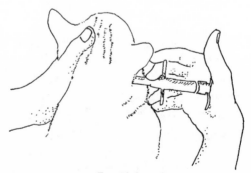

Fig. 12-9.
Toggling with the metal mallet.

recoil instrument. Just remember to spend a few practice squeezes with the mallet in the air to get your cat used to the clicking sound; otherwise he'll be startled by the adjustment.

METHOD FIVE: Posterior Atlas Adjustment (JM).
Note: FOR PROFESSIONAL USE ONLY.

This move is among my favorites. Feel both atlas wings and determine which side is higher. In this case, "higher" doesn't mean the wing feels bigger on the side of your cat's neck, as described for the toggle moves. Higher here means the top of one side of the neck feels bigger and spongier (Fig. 12-10). For the posterior atlas, you will simply feel which side of the neck directly below the base of the skull feels harder, or pushed upwards. For example, if you were to place two cotton balls, a

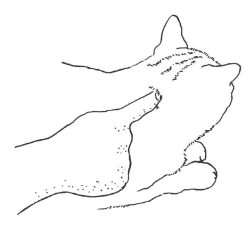

Fig. 12-10.
Feeling the "high side" of the atlas. The high side is palpated beneath the base of the skull. (In this example, the right side is high.)

big and a small one, under a piece of paper and right next to each other, you would be able to feel which one is larger. That's the posterior atlas. The wing has moved up, or posterior. Veterinarians would use the term *dorsal* instead of *posterior* to describe this subluxation.

Let's take a specific misalignment: a posterior atlas on the right. Therefore, if the right atlas wing has moved up, then the left wing must have moved down, that is, anterior (ventral) or closer to the throat (Fig. 12-11). The cat with a posterior atlas doesn't always display obvious signs of neck pain or unusual neck contortions. This is something you have to feel for yourself. Again, check the "yes" joint. If the cat veers his head more to the right during the "yes" check, he probably has a right posterior subluxation.

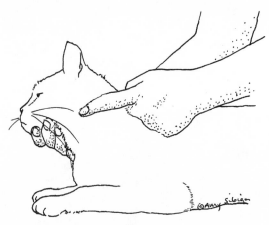

Fig. 12-11.
The lower atlas wing is palpated on the opposite side near the side of the neck, close to the jaw joint and the throat.

To correct the right posterior atlas, immobilize (stabilize) the second neck bone (axis) with your left hand, and grasp your cat's face with your right hand. To prevent the cat from biting you, grasp his face with a thin towel or wear a glove (even though I never do, since this gives you less control). Next, tuck the cat's neck down towards his chest and rotate (turn) his nose up towards the low atlas side, which is the side opposite the posterior wing (Fig. 12-12). Don't forget to keep his chin tucked down; otherwise you won't be able to take out all of the joint slack. After you've turned his nose all the way up so all of the joint slack is out (counterclockwise if you're facing him), complete the adjustment by quickly (*not* force-fully) turning his head up "one more notch," which will usually produce a slight popping sound or release. The adjustment is actually a quick snap of your wrist.

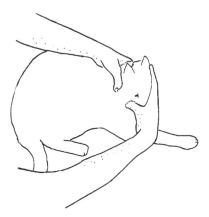

Fig. 12-12.
Stabilizing the second neck bone (axis) while tucking the head down for the right posterior atlas move.

METHOD SIX: Posterior Atlas Adjustment (MM). For this method, use the same palpation findings as in Method Five. The adjustment is done by placing the tip of the metal mallet on the high wing so it's pointing towards the low side of the atlas on the opposite side (Fig. 12-13). This is a high-speed/low-force adjustment, so just expose one or two rings below the mallet's collar. Once you've stabilized the opposite side of the head, squeeze the mallet's handle to deliver the thrust. Again, as with all metal mallet adjusting, the cat might react to the clicking sound. Nonetheless, this is a safe and effective way of adjusting which is also easy to do.

METHOD SEVEN: Axis Spine Adjustment (ST). Feel the base of your cat's skull (occiput) and drop your finger down about a half an inch. You will feel a bump which is the spine of the second neck bone (axis) (Fig. 12-14). Keep one finger on

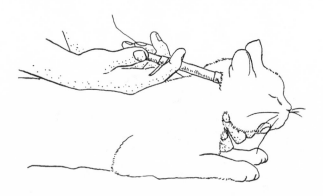

Fig. 12-13.
Adjusting the high atlas wing with the metal mallet.

this particular spine and rotate your cat's head back and forth, which tests the "no" motion. If your cat has difficulty moving his head "no" to the right, then the axis spine is probably stuck on the right. To help free up this bone, place the tip of your thumb on the right side of the axis spine and apply moderate pressure towards the left and hold for a full minute (Fig. 12-15). Note that your other hand is stabilizing the left side of your cat's head. After you're done, recheck the "no" joint.

METHOD EIGHT: Axis Toggle (JM/MM). The *axis* toggle is not fundamentally the same as the *atlas* toggle. The axis is part of a tighter or more restricted joint than the atlas, and it will *not* find its own level within the spinal column once set in motion. The axis toggle basically loosens the *atlanto-axial joint* (the joint comprised of the atlas and axis) to give your cat better neck rotation. Dogs, not cats, mainly suffer from upper

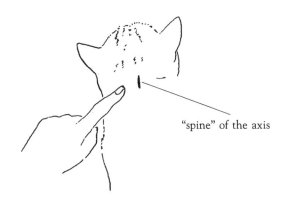

"spine" of the axis

Fig. 12-14.
Pointing to, and about to touch, the "spine" of the second cervical.

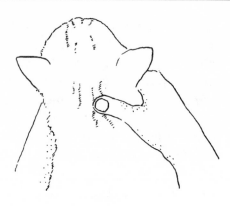

Fig. 12-15.
Applying thumb pressure to the "spine" of the axis (second neck bone).

neck problems due to their owner's misuse of collars. Cats, however, can experience upper neck pain due to unexpected maneuvering while running and chasing prey.

The first axis toggle method is done manually and is considered to be joint manipulation. The same tests apply here as in Method Seven. For an axis spine that is more prominent on the right, situate yourself next to your cat, place your right thumb tip on the axis spine and stabilize the left side of the head (see Fig. 12-15). Next, apply a sudden but not forceful punch, with your thumb contact aimed towards the left side of the neck. Make sure you push away all of the loose skin around the axis before delivering the punch. This is known as a tissue pull (push). Again, check the "no" joint when finished.

The second axis toggle method utilizes the metal mallet. Place the tip of the mallet on the right side of the axis spine as in the first axis toggle. Stabilize the left side of the head and squeeze the handle. As in most mallet methods, expose only one or two rings below the mallet's collar. The noise of the mallet may startle your cat, so don't be alarmed if he jumps. Recheck the "no" joint.

METHOD NINE: Axis Body/Traction Move (JM).
Note: FOR PROFESSIONAL USE ONLY.
This is my personal favorite feline axis move, and it can take the place of the above axis toggle methods. Again, test the "no" joint as above, with one exception; if your cat has a harder time rotating his head to the right and it's *not* due to the axis spine moving towards the right, then maybe it's the *body* of the axis that is misaligned. To check the body of the axis (or for that matter, any other cervical body), place the knife edge of your index finger next to the axis body (which is situated at the mid-side of the neck (Fig. 12-16) and laterally bend the neck over your finger (Fig. 12-17). Do this on both sides of the

Fig. 12-16.
Palpating the side of the neck to feel the "bodies" of the vertebrae.

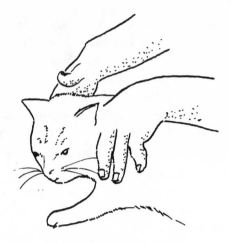

Fig. 12-17a.
Checking for a "fixed" neck joint. This example shows how to test for
the second neck bone (axis).

Fig. 12-17b.
Bending the cat's neck to the left tests for "fixed" or stuck joints on the
left. Do the test on both sides.

neck for the same bone. If your cat's neck bends less on the right, then you can apply Method Nine.

To perform this method, situate yourself in front of your cat while an assistant holds the back side of the cat still (Fig. 12-18). For a right axis body rotation, place the knife edge of your left index finger on the axis body. Your right hand will contact the left side of your cat's head and neck. Then, with both hands, gently pull your cat's neck towards you (this is the traction that opens up the joint) and slightly rotate his head towards his left until all of the joint slack is removed. The adjustment is completed by delivering a combination of a quick pull and a counterclockwise impulse. This will normally produce an audible or a popping sound.

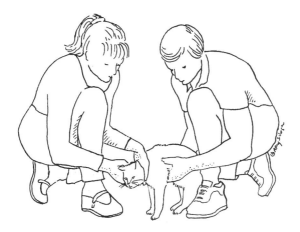

Fig. 12-18.
For some neck moves, an assistant holds the cat still while the practitioner delivers the adjustment. **Note:** This diagram does not depict a specific adjustment.

The difference between executing this move on a cat and on a dog is that the cat's neck is much more flexible, which makes taking the joint to "tension" more difficult. The first time I attempted this move, I thought the cat's neck could be twisted around my finger 180 degrees, like an owl's. So that this doesn't happen to you, just laterally bend the cat's neck a little more over your finger before you rotate the head to tension. The joint will stop a lot sooner.

METHOD TEN: Cervical Body Method (JM). The cervical body method is exactly the same as the axis body/traction move and can be applied to the rest of the neck bones. The only difference is that your cat has more lateral flexion at the mid- and lower neck bones than with the axis. You therefore have to laterally bend his neck more to check for body rotation and during the adjustment.

METHOD ELEVEN: Cervical Body Method (ST): If you'll notice, there are no specific neck adjustments below the axis that require contacting a cervical "spine." This is because you cannot feel most of the cervical spines except on the second neck bone (axis) and on the last one (seventh cervical). The seventh neck bone adjusts more like one of the upper middle back bones (a.k.a. thoracics, or dorsals) and is covered in the next chapter.

To do a soft tissue cervical body method, simply find the side of least lateral flexion, place your index finger on the "fixed" joint and gently bend your cat's neck over that finger. Hold for about twenty seconds and release (Fig. 12-19).

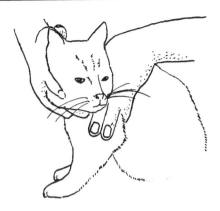

Fig. 12-19.
Bending the neck to the side (lateral flexion) to release
tension in the neck.

METHOD TWELVE: Cervical Body Method (MM). If you
want to apply an impulse into the fixed cervical body without
first tractioning the joint as in Method Nine, simply find the
rotated body, apply the tip of the mallet on that point, stabilize
the opposite side of the neck with your other hand, and squeeze
the handle. **Note:** In my experience, it doesn't appear to make
a whole lot of difference if you take the cat's neck to tension
here. The action of the mallet is fast enough to successfully
move the cervical bodies without taking out the joint slack.

METHOD THIRTEEN: General Cervical Traction (ST).
This is just what it says: traction. It should be applied *very
lightly*, which is why it's considered a soft tissue method. If you
notice that your cat is always twitching his head as if to shake
off water, he may be experiencing minor neck discomfort. To

release muscular stress in your cat's neck, situate yourself in front of your cat with an assistant stabilizing him at the rear (Fig. 12-20). With both hands, gently contact the side of his neck with the knife edge of both index fingers, then gradually and gently pull towards yourself. Hold the traction for about ten seconds, then release. As long as you don't pull too hard, you can apply this method on several neck bones within a five-minute time span without hurting your cat.

METHOD FOURTEEN: Pressure Points and Trigger Points (ST). These methods are easily implemented and are as safe as most massage techniques. First of all, pressure points are not the same as trigger points. A pressure point is a hard spot of a muscle that is "broken up" by applying moderate and steady

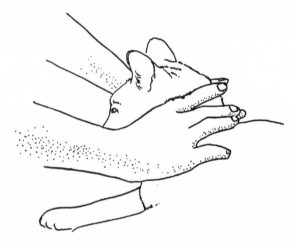

Fig. 12-20.
General neck traction move.

finger pressure into it. The areas of the muscle that is hard is usually the *belly* or center of the muscle. If you feel hard or irregular muscle knots on your cat's neck, press into each one for a few seconds (about ten) and release. This will help the muscles only in the area of the knot. If your cat is particularly tense, he'll have a lot of these knots that need to be treated. But you'll be amazed how relaxed your cat will be when you're done.

Trigger points often feel the same as pressure points, but they are different. When pressed, a trigger point will affect another part of the body. For example, if you have arm pain, you may have a hard muscle knot behind your neck that's causing the arm pain. When you press this spot on the neck, you might feel a sensation traveling down your arm. This is the "bad fuse" that's causing the lights to dim. Therefore, if you notice your cat struggling to walk on his front legs, and there's nothing functionally wrong with the legs, then feel for hard muscles around his lower neck and shoulders. Once you find one, gently press into it for a few seconds and release (Fig. 12-21). Then watch him walk again. You will sometimes notice immediate results.

METHOD FIFTEEN: Skin Lifting and Skin Rolling (ST). This is more of a physiotherapy than a chiropractic procedure; however, it fits well with the pressure and trigger point methods. If you feel a hard muscle knot and your cat is too sore to press, then simply grasp the skin over this knot and lift up as far as its elasticity will allow. Hold for a few seconds and release. This reduces the friction between the skin, the muscles, and

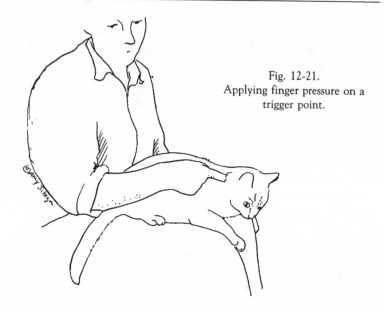

Fig. 12-21.
Applying finger pressure on a
trigger point.

the *myofascia*—a sheet of fibrous tissue surrounding the muscles found under the skin. With muscle knots and spasms, there will often be adhesions between the skin and the muscles. By lifting/stretching up the skin and then rolling it (like a cigarette), you release some of these adhesions, which reduces muscle stress.

A NOTE ABOUT MASSAGING

How often do you ask someone to give you a good hard massage? If you're an active person who works out in the gym, chances are you like a hard massage. But is this really good for you?

The main purpose of massage is to increase blood flow to the muscles, which in turn increases oxygen flow. It's this increase of oxygen to the muscle that causes it to relax. The action of massaging is this: When you compress a muscle, you temporarily squeeze out the blood which draws oxygen out of the muscle. This causes the muscle to "gasp for air." So when you release the pressure on the muscle, its first reaction is to open up its blood chambers (vessels) and flood itself with blood, thus holding even more oxygen than before the massage and overcompensating for the temporary loss. But you don't have to knead the muscle like dough to accomplish this. In fact, the opposite is true. Even a hard muscle knot is a delicate structure, and by pressing too hard, it is possible to damage the muscle fibers. A lighter but longer massage is much healthier than a short, harsh one.

CHAPTER 13

METHODS TO HELP
YOUR CAT'S MID~BACK

It almost seems impossible that anything could go wrong with your cat's mid-back, since it's so flexible. But subluxations don't always show signs of lameness. Your cat's mid-back can be harboring nerve interference that's eating away at his digestive system, lungs, heart, etc. And it's up to you to find and treat these subluxations in the absence of professional chiropractic care.

Anatomically, you can separate the middle spine from its associated parts such as the ribs, scapulas, chest, and forelegs, but functionally they're all related. Hence, when you study these methods, remember that subluxations in the thoracic (mid-back) area may be caused by a rib injury, a rigid scapula, or even a carpus (wrist) ailment, which is a foreleg condition. Methods to help these areas are discussed in Chapter 16.

METHOD ONE: Pressure Points and Trigger Points (ST). Review the explanation of these methods as given at the end of Chapter 12. The reason I list the pressure and trigger point methods first in this chapter is because these are often all you need to rid your cat of mid-back subluxations, and you don't need to deliver a thrust. Muscle knots flanking the spines of the mid-back usually indicate subluxations caused by activity associated with minor traumas (i.e. falling from a table or tree), or by *lack* of activity—sleeping the whole day in one place.

Lack of movement, as endured by caged or pampered animals, causes the back muscles to atrophy and become less vital. During those short bursts of inspiration when your cat finally decides to get off his tail, the muscles aren't prepared to handle the sudden maneuvers and they kink at assorted locations to brace the body. So even when you think your cat couldn't possibly have subluxated himself, he has!

For this method, scan both sides of your cat's middle back with your fingertips, and locate the muscle knots. When you find one, press the tip of your finger into it and apply moderate pressure for about twenty seconds, then release. Do this for all the tight muscle spots. If a muscle feels suspiciously hard, it may not be a muscle at all, but a rib. You'll know if it is a rib if this bump is part of a hard line that can be traced to the chest and the spine.

METHOD TWO: Pushing the Spines (ST). To review: the term "spines" refers to the tops of the vertebrae, or the pointy tips you can feel on the cat's back. This method involves applying pressure into the laterally deviated spine. The first step is to determine which spine feels off center. Starting at the end of the neck near the shoulders (seventh cervical), place the tip of your index finger here and slowly feel all the way down your cat's mid-back until you reach the end of the ribs. Did all of these spines feel like they made a straight line, or did your finger want to veer off to one side of the spines during the scan? If you're not sure, then scan the thoracics again, only this time with your thumb on one side of the spines and your index finger on the other side (see Fig. 3-22). This will let you read both sides at once. If you're still not sure, then simply palpate the muscles on the side of each spine. The harder side is the side of the deviated or lateral spine. Thus, a hard muscle to the right of one of these spines means that spine is pushed more to the right and needs to be adjusted to the left.

The adjustment for a mid-back spine deviated to the right is performed by first making a fist (which secures your thumb against the rest of your fingers), then placing your thumb tip against the misaligned spine and applying moderate but steady pressure for 30 seconds (make sure your other hand stabilizes the cat underneath on the chest or abdomen). The pressure is applied in three directions at once: right to left, down (dorsal to ventral, in veterinary terms), and in the direction of the spine itself. As you may recall from Chapter 3 (The Physical Feline), the mid-back spines take on many directions as they make their way towards the low back. The upper thoracics point towards the tail, and the lower ones point more towards the sky. While pushing the spines, your thumb and wrist should be extensions of the spines, thus complementing the natural angle of the vertebrae (Fig. 13-1).

METHOD THREE: Pushing the Spines (JM). The same set-up is used for this method as in Method Two, but instead of pushing the spines, you're delivering a quick punch or impulse into the spine. To adjust the upper thoracics, you will some-

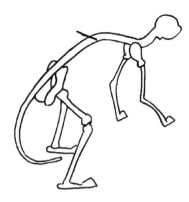

Fig. 13-1a.
This diagram depicts a spinous process, or "spine," pointing toward the tail.

Fig. 13-1b.
The angle of your adjusting hand for the upper and mid-thoracics should
be an extension of the spinous.

times have to lift up on the cat's chest to expose the upper thoracic spines since the scapulas may be "hiding" them (Fig. 13-2).

METHOD FOUR: Pushing The Spines (MM). What could be easier? Simply adjust the tension on the metal mallet to two rings below the collar, and apply the tip to the deviated spine. Line up the mallet as your thumb was lined up in Method Two, and squeeze the mallet's handle once.

As you can see, the metal mallet is a fairly handy instrument. You can even get spoiled by using it. It's sort of the Swiss

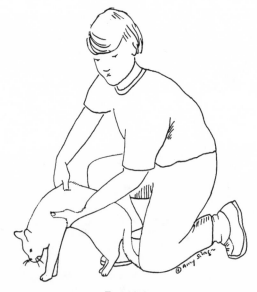

Fig. 13-2.
Lifting up on the chest helps expose the spinous processes ("spines").

Army Knife of feline as well as canine adjusting—and it's perfectly legal to buy one. However, you'll never become a skilled adjuster if you always depend on the mallet. Delivering the adjustment by hand gives you a better appreciation of chiropractic and is more satisfying to you and your cat. Hippocrates never talked about the laying on of metal!

METHOD FIVE: Releasing the Fixations (JM). Here is a move you can *only* do by hand. The first step is to find the joint fixation, that is, the one that's stuck. Start at the bottom of the neck (where the mid-back begins), placing the tip of your thumb on one side of the spines and the tip of your index finger on the other side. With a steady and moderately deep rhythm going, bounce down the spine and determine which joint has less spring to it. This is the fixed one that needs to be adjusted. Of course, there may be more than one fixed joint in the mid-back. To release this fixation, flank this spine with your thumb and index finger, gradually press deeply into the joint until it stops, then emit a sudden impulse. Your other hand is supporting the cat from underneath. You will often feel a "pop" with this method.

METHOD SIX: Spinal Traction (JM). This method doesn't actually involve delivering a thrust, but it's closer to being a joint manipulation method than a soft tissue technique. This procedure simply stretches your cat's back for him. To do this, place your cat on his belly on a carpeted floor. Have an assistant hold the cat's shoulders while you grasp the hindquarters, or vice versa. Then, simply stretch the front limbs up towards the head and the hind limbs towards the tail (Fig. 13-3). Hold this position for about ten seconds, release, and repeat again. The carpeted floor provides friction, preventing the cat from slipping during the procedure.

METHOD SEVEN: Skin Lifting and Skin Rolling (ST). Review Chapter 12, Method 15 (pages 149-150).

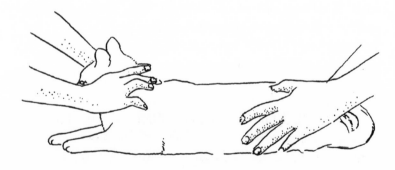

Fig. 13-3.
Gentle back traction.

CHAPTER 14

METHODS TO HELP YOUR CAT'S LOWER BACK

Your cat's lower back is just as elastic as his middle spine, if not more so. But the muscles tend to splint those areas of greatest movement during overexertion and injuries. Also, subluxations in your cat's lower back can cause a variety of internal ailments including bladder and bowel dysfunction (see Chapter 1). Even when a cat is hurting, his lower back may show no signs of lameness due to its incredible flexibility. This is why you must look for and treat lower spine subluxations, especially when the vet says there's no medical reason for your cat's bladder condition.

METHOD ONE: Pushing the Spines (ST). This is very similar to the mid-back methods. The main difference between applying this technique in the lumbars and in the thoracics is that the lumbars are not bound by ribs, which makes them feel bouncier when pushed. Additionally, a lumbar spine that is off-centered to one side or the other is less noticeable by touch. A deviated spine in the thoracics is anchored by the ribs which makes this finding consistent, while a deviated spine in the lumbars can fluctuate depending on the position of the cat.

If you're able to determine by touch that a lumbar spine is misaligned to the right, for example, then situate yourself next to your cat and place your thumb on the right side of that particular spine and push right to left. Hold this moderate pressure for about 30 seconds. Don't forget to stabilize your cat underneath his abdomen (Fig. 14-1).

METHOD TWO: Pushing the Spines (JM): Use the same findings as in Method One, only instead of applying pressure to the spine for 30 seconds, contact the right side of the spine with your right thumb tip while keeping your wrist and elbow rigid. Then deliver a quick impulse/punch straight across, right

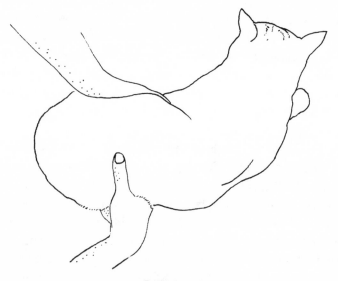

Fig. 14-1.
Applying thumb pressure on a mid-lumbar spinous.

to left, while stabilizing the cat underneath (see Fig. 14-1). Here again, you must consider several factors dictating the direction of your thrust, as described in the middle back methods. Since the lumbar spines point towards the sky and somewhat towards the head, your thrust or impulse direction for a lumbar spine deviated to the right is: right to left, down (dorsal to ventral), and slightly "up" towards the cat's head.

METHOD THREE: Pushing the Spines (MM): Same as Method Two, except you deliver the impulse with the metal mallet.

METHOD FOUR: Lumbar Extension/Traction (JM). This general lower-back mobilization move requires an assistant. If your cat seems to be dragging his lower legs while walking, or is running slower than before, he might have some tightness in his lower back. Of course, there may be more serious things wrong with him, such as a herniated disc or a neurological condition, where veterinary care would be required (see Chapter 8—Contraindications).

The lumbar extension/traction move is done by situating yourself behind your standing cat. Grasp high on both thighs so both of your index fingers are contacting the abdomen. Your thumbs should be free to press near the spines (Fig. 14-2). Next, lift and extend the hind legs backward and place both of your thumbs next to the first lumbar (one thumb per side) (Fig. 14-3). Your assistant (should you use one) does *not* lift the front end up into the air; rather, the front legs and feet should maintain continuous contact with the floor or table. After this, gently pull the cat towards yourself (this is the traction) and press into the spinal area until it stops. This takes out the joint slack. Then, impulse down into the spine with a sudden flick of your wrist. Continue this process in rapid succession for every other lumbar spine until you reach the last one. You may notice some joint movement accompanying the adjustment.

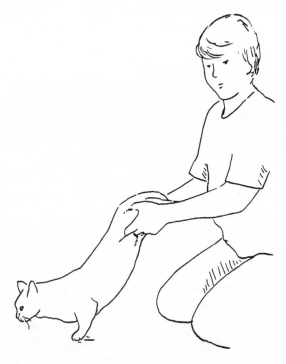

Fig. 14-2.
Situate yourself behind your cat for the lumbar extension move.

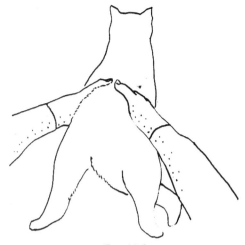

Fig. 14-3.
Lift your cat's hind legs off the floor and gently push down on the lumbars. **Note:** If your cat resists this method, do NOT repeat; use an alternative technique.

METHOD FIVE: Lumbar Roll (JM). This is a standard feline chiropractic move that sometimes requires an assistant. The lumbar roll is considered a general lower-back mobilization technique, but with skillful and professional execution, it can be specific for one lumbar joint.

The mechanics of the lumbar roll are somewhat different for a cat than a person. When a person's lumbars are "rolled," they are placed on their side, all of the slack is removed from the spine (taking the joint to tension), and the practitioner thrusts down and across the patient (Fig. 14-4). There is more slack to take out of a person's lumbar spine since they have an

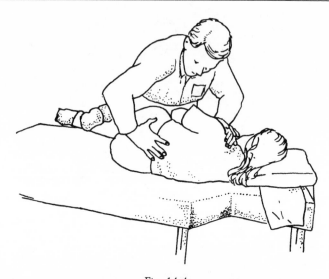

Fig. 14-4.
Human lumbar roll. This releases lower back tension.

inward lumbar curve (small of the back), jutting towards their abdomen. Cats and dogs don't have this.

To give your cat a lumbar roll, place him on his back. Situate yourself behind the cat and grasp both thighs as high as you can until your hands touch the abdomen. Extend both legs towards you. This tractions the lumbars, which opens up the joint spaces. Have an assistant stabilize the cat by pressing down on the chest. The adjustment is made by quickly bringing both legs down to one side while the front of the cat is immobilized by the assistant (Fig. 14-5). Repeat by pushing the legs down towards the other side. Most cats are small enough that you can do this move without an assistant.

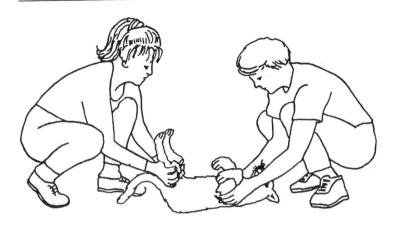

Fig. 14-5a.
Assistant is stabilizing the front of the cat for the lumbar roll.

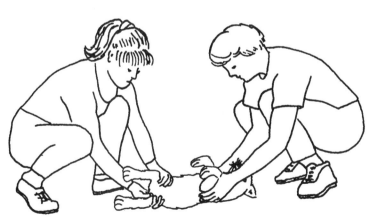

Fig. 14-5b.
Both of the cat's legs are brought down to one side for the lumbar roll.

Here are a couple of hints you can use to make the lumbar roll more effective. The first one is that while you're bringing both legs down to one side, you or your assistant should push the front of the cat (under the armpits) in the opposite direction to create a "scissors" action. This will "wring out" even more slack from the lower spine.

The second hint should be done if you want only one joint to move. Let's say you want to mobilize the joint created by the 6th and 7th lumbar. What you do is massage the muscles over that joint for about 30 seconds prior to delivering the lumbar roll. This will temporarily weaken and exhaust the joint, which will make it the first one to move during the procedure. Then, have your assistant or yourself immobilize all of the lumbars above that joint by placing your hand low on the abdomen. By "nailing" all the other lumbars down with your hand, the only joints free to move would be the last ones.

METHOD SIX: Skin Lifting and Skin Rolling (ST). Review Chapter 12, pages 149-150, for these methods.

CHAPTER 15

METHODS TO HELP YOUR CAT'S HIPS AND BELOW

Aside from the spine, most chiropractors adjust other bones and joints which affect the overall performance of the cat. The pelvis, sacrum (which is the bone directly below the last lumbar and right before the tail), and hip socket are among the most commonly adjusted extra-vertebral bones. **Note:** Some anatomists consider the sacrum part of the spinal column.

Let's first identify the parts you'll be contacting during the hip adjustments. There are primarily two points on the hip bone you'll touch for certain hip adjustments. One part is the top of the hip, known as the Posterior-Superior-Iliac Spine (PSIS); the other part is the hip socket, or *acetabulum* (hip joint) (Fig. 15-1). Whenever you hear of someone getting a hip replacement, they don't have their whole hip bone replaced with a new one, they merely have the hip socket replaced, along with the head of the femur (thigh bone) which forms a ball and socket joint.

Unlike certain dog breeds, cats don't get hip dysplasia, which is an unstable ball and socket joint caused by a shallow acetabulum. However, cats do experience pain in the hip socket, usually caused by falls. There is some debate over whether the

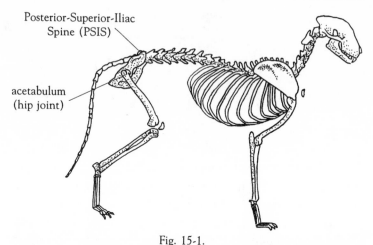

Fig. 15-1.
The two areas of the hip and pelvis that are regularly adjusted are the acetabulum (hip socket) and the PSIS (the top of the pelvis).

hip joint should be adjusted at all. The concern some chiropractors have against adjusting the hip socket is that if the joint has been injured, as with a fall, then the joint would be unstable and loose, negating and contraindicating the need for manipulation. I agree with this. However, after a period of time, the soft tissues heal, and the aftermath may be a slow, rusty joint that needs to be "oiled up" by gently loosening up the ligamentous adhesions through manipulation.

METHOD ONE: Ligament Push (ST). In this author's opinion, the ligament push is the single most effective move in this book as far as overall healing potential. It is also one of the easiest to do and is very safe. However, don't get the impression that you can perform this move and forsake all others. The ligament push accomplishes a whole lot all at once, but not everything.

The ligament push is also known as Logan Basic Technique. It is so effective that the Logan College of Chiropractic, which is located in St. Louis, Missouri, developed an entire teaching system around this procedure. A skillfully executed ligament push will help relieve low-back pain, balance the spinal fluid (which affects the entire body), reduce stress in the hips and legs, improve bowel and bladder conditions, and even help neck pain! (Neck pain is sometimes the result of neck muscles compensating for low-back pain.)

The structure that is contacted is the *sacrotuberous* ligament, a broad ligament that spans from the apex of the sacrum to the bottom of the hip (Fig. 15-2). The actual point of contact is above the anus at "1:00 o'clock" for a right contact, and "11:00 o'clock" for a left contact. Examination findings similar to those described in Chapter 14 (lower back methods) are used to determine which side to contact. For example, if you notice hard rump and lower back muscles on the right side, and your short leg analysis is positive for the right, then you contact the right sacrotuberous ligament. "Where there's the strain, there's the pain."

To administer this procedure, situate yourself behind your standing cat and lift up his tail. After you've determined which side to treat (the right side, for example), position your hand as if you're about to throw a football. Place your right thumb underneath the base of the tail and on the tip (apex) of the sacrum, which is the only palpable part of the sacrum (Fig. 15-3). You'll feel a tight, rubber band-like structure. This is the

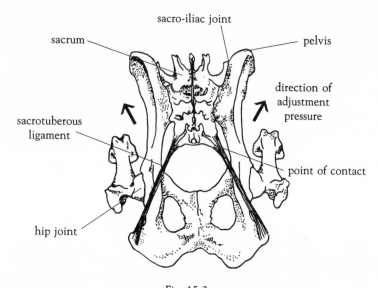

Fig. 15-2.
(Back view of cat) The sacrotuberous ligament contact
for the Ligament Push.

sacrotuberous ligament. Begin the treatment by gently pushing into this spot up towards the ear of the same side (the right ear in this example), and hold that light pressure for about a minute. The rest of your fingers are cradling the rump and are also pointed toward the right ear. The amount of pressure needed for a successful adjustment is not much, and is often likened to the maximum amount of force you can apply over your eyeball (with your eye closed) without damaging it. You're pressing too hard if your cat's tail becomes erect, or if his lower legs buckle.

During the minute that you're applying the pressure, you'll frequently notice the rump and lower back muscles will start to

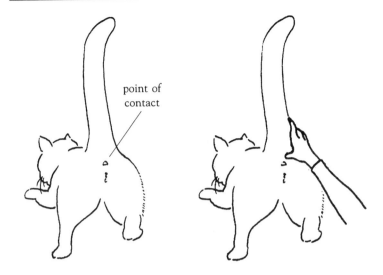

point of
contact

Fig. 15-3.
The Ligament Push applied (right side).

quiver. Lightly massage these shaking muscles until they calm down. After the minute has passed, apply a quick and final impulse or punch (in the same direction as the pressure— towards the right ear) and release. Logan practitioners often notice dramatic results directly following this procedure.

One last thought about the Ligament Push: **DO NOT, I repeat, DO NOT use the metal mallet here** (unless of course you want your cat to bite your hand from either end).

METHOD TWO: Hip Pull (JM). This easy manipulative technique helps restore the function of the hip socket. If your cat is limping on one or both of his hind legs and there is no evidence of bone or tissue damage, you might want to check the hip sockets for restricted motion. To do this, have your cat lie on his side (suspected painful side up). Next, place a finger or thumb of one hand on the hip socket and grasp the thigh bone (femur) while moving it backwards and forwards. The hip socket should glide smoothly during this test. If you feel any resistance from the hip socket, you'll need to adjust it.

Here's what you do: Situate yourself next to your cat (he's lying on his side with the painful side up); then, with one finger (or thumb), press into the head of the femur which fits into the socket (Fig. 15-4). Next, pull the thigh with your other hand and hold for about 10 seconds, then release. Make sure not to *jerk* the leg.

METHOD THREE: Hip Joint Push (JM/MM). The set-up for this method is the same as for Method Two. The difference is that you deliver a push into the head of the femur while the

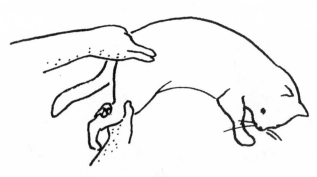

Fig. 15-4.
The Hip Pull move.

thigh is being pulled. The push is a quick impulse discharged from either your thumb or the metal mallet. Set the mallet at three rings below the collar for a little extra force.

METHOD FOUR: Hip Roll (JM). This move is intended to free up the sacro-iliac joint (see Chapter 3). You cannot feel the base of the sacrum (the base is that part of the sacrum closest to the last lumbar), because it's deeply imbedded between the two pelvic bones. However, you can test and adjust the joint formed by the hip and the sacrum (sacro-iliac joint). To test for a fixed sacro-iliac joint, lay your cat on his belly, all stretched out with his forelegs above his head and his hind legs fully extended back (Fig. 15-5). Next, individually push down on the top of each hip bone (PSIS) and determine if the cat experiences pain (by whining or flinching), or if one joint simply felt less springy than the other. Also, refer back to the

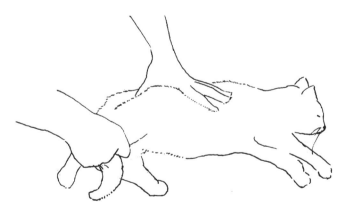

Fig. 15-5.
The Hip Roll: testing and adjusting the sacro-iliac joint.

short-leg analysis in Chapter 7 to determine which hip is distressed. This is the one you adjust.

To perform the hip roll on your cat, have him lie on his side with the painful side up. Contact the top of the hip with the heal of your hand, and extend the thigh of the same side (the *ipsolateral* leg) backwards until it stops (see Fig. 15-5). At this point, deliver a quick but not forceful punch (impulse) into your contact (top of hip). Immediately remove your hands. You will sometimes feel a release or pop with this move.

METHOD FIVE: Unilateral Hip Push (MM). Situate yourself behind your cat and with both thumbs contact each PSIS (the top of each hip) with the metal mallet. Adjust the tops of the hips with the metal mallet, one hip at a time. **Note:** For this method, the mallet should be set three rings below the collar.

METHOD SEVEN: Sacrum Push (ST). The *sacrum* is the bone immediately below the last low-back (lumbar) vertebra. As previously mentioned, you can't always feel the sacrum since it is wedged between the two pelvic bones, but you can feel the web of soft tissue over it. The sacrum push is simply done by placing the tip of your finger into this space and applying moderate pressure for about 30 seconds while supporting your cat underneath (Fig. 15-6). This will help relieve low back pain, and sometimes ease bowel and bladder dysfunctions. If you could directly push on the sacrum without the obstructing soft tissue, it would act as a lever which tractions the lumbars and reduces low-back pain.

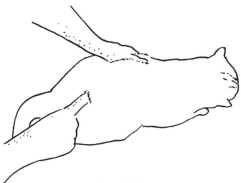

Fig. 15-6.
The Sacrum Push applied. Even though it's not always possible to feel the sacrum, you can relieve lower back muscle spasms by putting light pressure in the space between the pelvic bones.

METHOD EIGHT: Tail Traction (JM). This method is so gentle that it can be classified as a soft tissue method. But since the adjustment requires a little "tug," it is listed as joint manipulation. We've all pulled our cats' tails as kids. Were we adjusting them? Well, yes and no (depending on the glint in our eye during the treatment).

Cats use their tails for a lot things such as balance and expressing emotions. And because they use their tails so much, there is the potential for tail stress or tension. When this occurs, the tail needs to be adjusted. Since cats have an average of about 20 tail bones, which are small and delicate, you have to use caution while adjusting them. *Never yank the tail.* The right way to adjust the tail is to hold the rump still with one hand, and with your other hand, grasp the tail firmly at the base (root), where it comes off the rump. Rotate with a gentle circular motion for ten seconds (Fig. 15-7). At the end of the ten seconds, apply a firm tug. If the cat tries to bite you during this procedure, stop doing it. He's telling you that something is wrong.

This move may be a little difficult to administer on a Manx (a tail-less breed). Since you're required to contact the tail at the root, you might end up doing Logan Basic instead!

Fig. 15-7.
Never yank the tail. Always support the tail near its base
when applying traction.

CHAPTER 16

METHODS TO HELP
YOUR CAT'S OTHER JOINTS

Thus far you've learned to treat subluxations associated with your cat's spine and hips. But think about the other skeletal parts. Are they prone to subluxations? Do they need to be adjusted? The answer to both these questions is "yes." A chiropractic purist will say that only the spine contains true subluxations. But the practitioner of chiropractic should think of the body as a whole, and treat holistically. This means restoring normal joint function wherever needed. This includes the extremities which consists of those skeletal parts not belonging to or directly attaching to the spine.

A vertebral subluxation, which is a spinal nerve pinched between adjacent vertebrae, is the classic example of how nerve pressure causes stress in the body. But other skeletal structures—such as the jaw, scapulas, elbows, wrists, digits, and ribs—must also function smoothly within their normal confinements; if not, the spine as well as the whole body will suffer. By "cleaning up" these other areas, you are allowing the feline machine to function as a whole. Your car can still ride on a flat tire as long as the engine is running, but wouldn't you get a smoother ride if you fixed the flat?

The Jaw (ST)

Cats, like people and dogs, have one moveable joint on their head: the jaw joint, or *mandible*, which works like a hinge. This hinge joint can sometimes become stressed on a cat due to difficult tearing of food and tight jaw muscles (but not chewing. In fact, a cat cannot chew at all). You or someone you know may be afflicted with a condition known as TMJ (or TMD: Temporomandibular Joint/Disease), where the lower jaw is not properly aligned with the upper jaw. People suffering from this condition often visit their dentist to be fitted with a bite plate to help align their jaw.

For less serious TMJ conditions, people often visit chiropractors. Sometimes the jaw joint is just a little stuck and can be improved with manipulation. I've seen very little of this with cats, but at times you might notice your cat struggling to eat due to jaw pain. If so, feel both sides of his jaw where it hinges at the side of his head, and determine which overlying muscles feel harder (Fig. 16-1). I don't suggest you manipulate this area. Instead, press into the tighter muscle with the tip of your finger and hold moderate pressure there for about 20 seconds and release. Jaw problems are also associated with upper neck conditions, so check the upper cervicals as well.

The Shoulder Blades (JM/ST)

As runners, jumpers, climbers, and pouncers, cats are prone to shoulder pain. Luckily, the shoulder blades (scapulas) are easy to feel and adjust. There are two types of scapular adjustments. One is called the *medial scapular method*, and the other is called

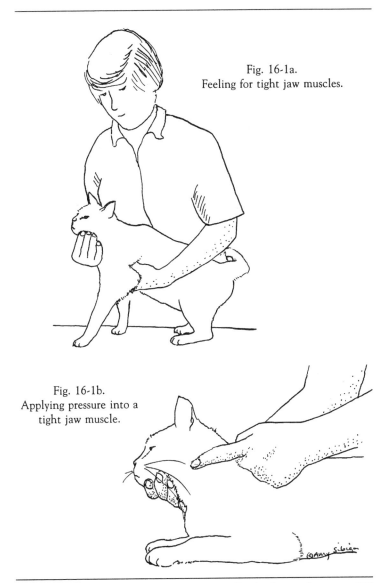

Fig. 16-1a.
Feeling for tight jaw muscles.

Fig. 16-1b.
Applying pressure into a
tight jaw muscle.

the *lateral scapular method.*

The medial scapular method is administered if you feel tight muscles surrounding the upper part of the shoulder blades next to the mid-back spines (Fig. 16-2). If so, then lift and flex the foreleg belonging to the sore shoulder blade. This creates a little space between the scapula and the muscles covering the ribs. With your other hand, lightly "dig" the tip of your index

Fig. 16-2a.
Feeling for tight muscles
surrounding the shoulder.

Fig. 16-2b.
Treating the muscles
around the scapula
(shoulder blade).

finger or thumb into this space and apply moderate pressure for about ten seconds. After the ten seconds are up, deliver a sudden impulse down towards the foreleg. This helps loosen up adhesions between the scapula and rib muscles, making ambulation easier.

The lateral scapular method is the technique of choice if you feel tight muscles over the top of the humerus where it meets the scapula (Fig. 16-3). (**Note:** The scapula does not form a true joint with the humerus.) If this is the case, flex the

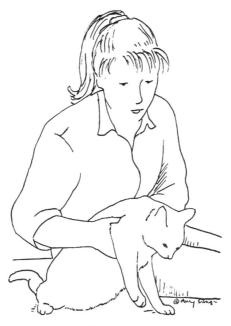

Fig. 16-3.
Feel the shoulder blade with your thumbs and lift up the leg to determine which side feels tighter, or exhibits less motion.

affected foreleg (until it stops) with one hand and stabilize the top of the scapula with the other. When you flex the foreleg, make sure you're grasping the humerus and not the wrist (carpus) (Fig. 16-4). Complete the adjustment by impulsing up on the flexed foreleg (humerus) towards the top of the spine. This, too, loosens up shoulder muscle adhesions. If you prefer, you may simply apply a light pressure point contact into the tight shoulder muscle.

The Elbow

This is a basic traction move. If you notice your cat limping on one of his forelegs, gently manipulate the affected elbow joint. Sit next to your cat, place a finger into the elbow joint, flex the joint around your finger, and hold for about five seconds (Fig. 16-5).

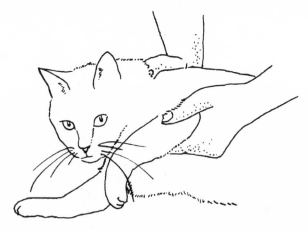

Fig. 16-4.
Lifting up on the foreleg to adjust the scapula.

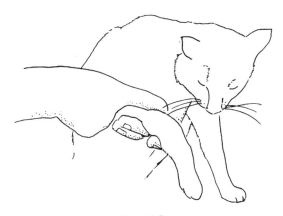

Fig. 16-5.
Gently manipulating the elbow joint.

The Wrists/Carpals (JM)

This is used for the lower part of the front legs. Cats, unlike dogs, are able to manipulate objects with their paws. Maintaining a supple wrist is essential. A cat who limps needs to have his wrist (carpus) manipulated.

Feel your cat's wrist, which is located under the forearm bones known as the *ulna* and *radius* (see Chapter 3). As a unit, the wrist bends quite easily. Grasp the affected paw with both your thumbs and index fingers, as if to give your cat a manicure. Begin by pulling the paw toward you (traction), and at the same time bend the paw in both directions (flexion and extension—down and up, respectively) (Fig. 16-6). Do this for about ten seconds per session. While working the wrist areas, you may want to see if the toes/digits or phalanges need loosening up. If so, then grasp them like you would the wrist and gently traction them in an up-and-down fashion. Or you may simply press the digits between your thumb and index finger (Fig. 16-7).

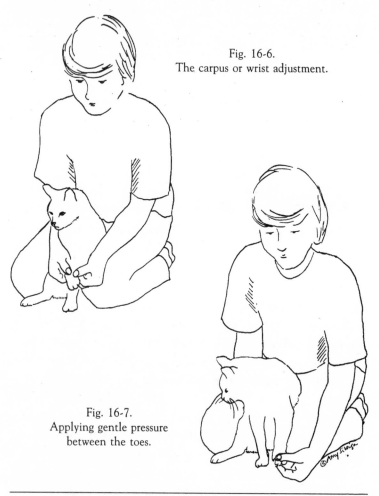

Fig. 16-6.
The carpus or wrist adjustment.

Fig. 16-7.
Applying gentle pressure
between the toes.

The Ribs

If your cat shows signs of labored breathing, the ribs may not be expanding properly. This is sometimes due to muscle spasms at the places where the ribs meet the mid-back bones (thoracic vertebrae), or where they meet the chest bone (sternum).

After your cat has had a vigorous run, place both hands on his mid-back. Note whether one side expands a little less than the other during inhalation. If so, feel the muscles and "rib bumps" just to the left or right of the thoracic "spines." If one feels higher, apply firm finger pressure (Fig. 16-8). Continue applying this pressure until your cat has taken fifteen or more deep breaths. (Your cat is, in effect, assisting with his own treatment.) Now turn your cat around so he's lying on his back. Place your hand on his chest bone (sternum) and allow him to take some deep breaths. Feel the sides of the chest bone with your fingertips. This is where the front part of the ribs meet. If you notice an elevation here, apply firm finger pressure and wait for your cat to take several more deep breaths.

As always, before attempting any sort of manipulation on your cat, consult your veterinarian to make sure there are no broken bones or other serious conditions.

Fig. 16-8a.
Lightly pressing into a high rib bump—which is usually a hard muscle knot.

Fig. 16-8b.
Applying light pressure over a tight muscle knot near the sternum (breastbone).

Fig. 16-8c.
Releasing muscle tension near the sternum (breastbone) can make breathing easier.

CHAPTER 17

METHODS TO HELP
YOUR CAT'S INSIDES AND
ASSORTED MUSCULOSKELETAL
CONDITIONS

It's somewhat ironic that the chapter on how to help your cat's insides appears near the end of this book. Most chiropractors seem preoccupied with treating back and neck pain, all but forgetting about internal conditions. Why? Are they afraid the AMA will raise a condescending eyebrow at them?

The question of "why" is strictly about money and nothing else. For over thirty years, human chiropractic services have been covered by many major health insurance carriers as well as auto and worker's compensation insurance. Almost all of the chiropractic diagnostic codes used on the various insurance forms reflect a musculoskeletal condition—mostly low-back and neck pain. There's nothing wrong with this, because chiropractors are in fact back pain specialists. But this just scratches the surface. Chiropractors have adapted to their market to please the patient—and to please the insurance companies, who would not cover their services if they claimed to help liver disorders.

Chiropractic has clinically been proven helpful for many

internal conditions in both people and animals. Among the most common internal conditions helped through chiropractic care are bladder and bowel dysfunction, gastrointestinal disorders, colic in infants, fevers (by boosting the body's resistance) migraines, kidney problems, liver conditions, and asthma—just to name a few. Now before you bring yourself or your cat to a chiropractor to have any of the above treated, get a medical opinion first. You see, chiropractors don't specifically treat the above conditions. They find and remove vertebral subluxations that hinder the body's own natural healing powers. Once the subluxation is treated, the body has a better chance to heal itself. If an internal (visceral) condition is in the acute or crisis stage, then it's too late for chiropractic care, and emergency medical intervention is needed.

The above statements represent a general opinion—mainly my own—on the efficacy of chiropractic. But a book of this nature has to side with caution. I don't want anyone to come away from this book thinking that the methods contained here can take the place of timely veterinary care. They can't. On the other hand, it's no coincidence that cats and other animals experience miraculous results for many internal problems with a properly delivered chiropractic adjustment.

Notice from the diagrams of the nervous system that specific vertebral areas control or influence certain organs. The lower lumbars, for example, exert control over the urinary system. So for bladder disorders, you would first examine the lower lumbars even though it's quite possible that an upper cervical subluxation could be a factor here.

WHERE TO "PUSH" FOR WHAT CONDITION

The above heading borders on being a little too simplistic, which it is. However, certain ailments "belong" to definite vertebral segments, or at least predictable spinal areas.

The following information was provided by Dr. William Inman, D.V.M., a veterinary chiropractor from Seattle, Washington who has treated over 15,000 pets with chiropractic methods over a period of ten years. Dr. Inman cites the following conditions as being helped through chiropractic care.

1. **Urinary and Fecal (Bowel) Incontinence:** These problems are indigenous to older cats, especially if they have been spayed or neutered. These problems are also common in the Manx, a mutant tail-less breed which is also predisposed to spina bifida (failure of a vertebra to close normally around the spinal cord). The spinal areas to adjust for lack of bowel and bladder control are the 4th, 5th, and 7th lumbars, as well as applying pressure over the sacrum.

2. **Reflux Esophagitis**: Problems associated with the *esophagus* (the long muscular tube extending from the mouth to the stomach), such as regurgitation, are thought to be caused by neurological interference. These cases respond particularly well with chiropractic care. The spinal levels involved here are the 2nd through 7th thoracic vertebrae. For best results, these subluxations should be treated twice a week for two months.

3. **Constipation and Diarrhea**: It is necessary to have your cat checked by a vet for other causes of gastrointestinal disorders, such as parasites and infections. The spinal areas commonly associated with constipation and diarrhea are the 4th, 5th, and 6th thoracic vertebrae.

4. **Ear and Eye Infections**: The nerves that control the eyes and the ears originate in the head (a.k.a. cranial nerves) and exit the head near the base of the skull. Therefore the vertebra most involved in ear and eye infections is the atlas, the first cervical vertebra. For chronic infections, you should treat the atlas subluxation weekly for about three months. Of course, your cat should also be receiving proper veterinary care.

OTHER DISORDERS (NOT INTERNAL)

1. **Unilateral Nerve Paralysis**: While not exactly an internal condition, nerve paralysis is important to note here. An example of this would be sciatica, a rear leg disorder that can cause lameness. If your cat is experiencing leg pain, he'll gnaw or bite the area in an effort to relieve the pain himself. The spinal areas involved here are the 4th, 5th, and 6th lumbars as well as the sacrum.

2. **Knee (Stifle) Disorders**: Subluxations of the 4th and 5th lumbar area often create muscular imbalances that affect the knee. If no patellar (kneecap) injury, bone, or soft tissue disorders are found, then adjust those

areas of the lower spine to help the knee.

3. **Disc Diseases**: According to Dr. Inman, "lapse, disc protrusion, blown disc, so-called slipped disc [herniations], and other disc phenomena are all treated alike. There is no reason for surgery unless the pet is in the process of paralysis or has been paralyzed for less than 24 hours. Surgery outside of the 24–48-hour window has no benefit as per current veterinary surgical literature." The most common sites for disc disease are at the 4th and 5th lumbar region, though they can occur anywhere. CAUTION: Use only low-force chiropractic methods for disc diseases, such as soft tissue and metal mallet techniques.

4. **Foreleg Lameness**: There are lots of reasons for foreleg lameness, though it is mainly seen with dogs, usually on one side. However, if your cat is favoring a front leg and there are no X-ray findings supporting bone or soft tissue damage, then look for subluxations at the 5th, 6th, and 7th cervical region as well as the 1st thoracic.

SYMPATHETIC AND PARASYMPATHETIC

You'll notice from the charts (Figs. 17-1, 17-2) that sometimes an organ, such as the stomach or heart, can be stimulated by adjusting different parts of the spine. One chart is "Sympathetic," the other "Parasympathetic." These terms refer to the parts of the *autonomic nervous system,* which works without your having to think about it (i.e., enabling you to breathe, or digest food while you sleep). Adjusting the stomach areas found

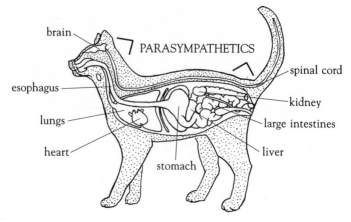

Fig. 17-1.
The nerves of the parasympathetic nervous system originate from the base of the head and from the sacrum (the area below the last lumbar and above the tail).

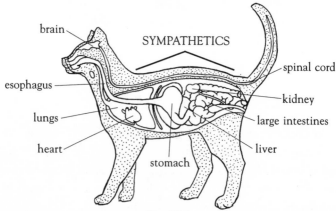

Fig. 17-2.
The nerves of the sympathetic nervous system originate from the first thoracic (dorsal) vertebra to the fifth lumbar.

on the parasympathetic chart will stimulate the stomach's function by increasing the amount of acid it produces, while relaxing the muscles around the rectum. The heart will calm down when you adjust the parasympathetic areas and speed up when you adjust the sympathetic areas. Therefore, by studying these charts, you'll have an idea of what the effect will be on your cat after the adjustment.

The sympathetics are also known as the "fight or flight" nervous system. During times of intense stress, your body releases more adrenaline (giving you supernatural strength in spite of having other ailments such as arthritic knees), and increases your heart rate and respiration. This gives you more ability to deal with the situation—you can either run or fight. The parasympathetics do just the opposite when stimulated. They calm you down. This is why you shouldn't exert yourself (swimming) after a meal. Your parasympathetics are busy during digestion, and exercise will kick-start the sympathetics, thus disrupting the digestive process.

THE METHODS

All of the methods you've learned in previous chapters can be applied when helping internal/visceral conditions. But for those of you who don't own a metal mallet, or simply don't feel confident enough to perform the manipulative procedures, you can still stimulate the vertebrae and reduce spinal nerve irritation by gently "thumping" the spines with your fingers. However, you must be specific and only stimulate one vertebra at a time. To do this, first determine which bone you want to treat.

Next, isolate that "spine" by straddling it with two fingers (Fig. 17-3), then thump it (like a watermelon) with the middle or index finger of the other hand (Fig. 17-4). The metal mallet is ideal for this use.

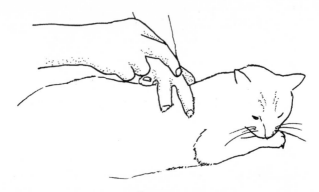

Fig. 17-3.
Preparing to thump a "spine" to stimulate a spinal nerve.

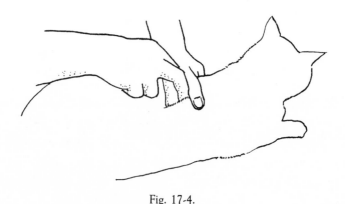

Fig. 17-4.
Thumping a "spine."

CHAPTER 18

CASE MANAGEMENT
AND CASE HISTORIES

Since you bought this book, you're obviously concerned about your cat's health. You've also shown some interest in helping your cat with chiropractic care. But remember, chiropractic is about managing vertebral subluxations, *not* medical conditions. Chiropractic does not take the place of veterinary medicine. You therefore have some decisions to make.

Is my cat a candidate for chiropractic care?

Providing your cat has recently had a thorough veterinary exam and was cleared of contraindications (see Chapter 8), then you may proceed with finding and removing subluxations.

Which spinal areas do I adjust?

You adjust the subluxations, wherever they are. One of the lessons I've learned in my sixteen years of practice is that a patient is entitled to more than one disease—in this case, subluxation. There are various degrees of nerve impingement, and even the smallest areas should be found and treated.

How many adjustments will it take for my cat to get well?

The average number of treatments (regular manipulation) for neck and back pain is four—which should be spread out over a two-week period. If you elect to use only the soft tissue techniques, then you can treat more often, even daily. Sometimes you have to use the "wait and see" approach. However, don't *over*-adjust. This will cause weak joints. But do check your cat on a regular basis for subluxations, even in the absence of pain. Maintenance care is the key word.

Should I adjust a cat who exhibits no symptoms?

Yes, you should. Pain is the *fifth phase* of the subluxation (see Chapter 2). By the time your cat experiences pain, the subluxation is already ingrained in his body. Regular spinal checks keep the subluxations in check!

Should I tell my vet about my cat's chiropractic care?

A resounding YES! Not only should you tell your veterinarian—let her borrow the book and give me a call. Your vet should be educated about chiropractic. If she's not interested in performing the procedures herself, put her in touch with someone who is, namely another vet or a neighboring chiropractor. The best possible health care alliance for your cat is regular veterinary *and* chiropractic care.

Will my cat's health always improve with chiropractic?

I would like to answer this with an unconditional "yes," but that wouldn't be honest. Not all conditions respond favorably with chiropractic. Finding and removing the subluxations is one piece of the health care puzzle. Dramatic results may occur, but you can't always expect them. Healing takes time: days, weeks, even months. Have patience with your patients.

THREE CASE HISTORIES

1. One of my favorite cats in the whole world is Gizmo, a four-year-old male shorthair who's been tormented most of his life due to his housemates. Gizmo is a declawed housecat who's afraid of anyone and everything. He has to put up with a giant and aggressive German shepherd, a monstrous macaw, and three other cats. His neck and back are in constant spasm. He's my favorite cat because I feel so sorry for him. His owner (Tom) is a friend of mine, and I'm always asking him to separate Gizmo from the rest of the herd. But my pleas fall on deaf ears.

    Nonetheless, Gizmo's main subluxation is the atlanto-occipital joint (the "yes" joint, between the base of the skull and the first neck bone). All body signals must pass through here on their way to the brain. A stressed-out cat like Gizmo will have a perpetual subluxation here unless the offending stresses are removed (such as all the other animals). Since Gizmo doesn't like to be touched, I'm very careful with him. I use only light touch, soft tissue moves on him. Since Gizmo and I are old buddies already, he knows I'm there to help him and doesn't mind being adjusted. My regular treatments are a right atlas release and the Ligament Push (Logan Basic Technique). After the adjustment, Gizmo takes a drink of water and falls asleep. Tom, however, did agree to let Gizmo "sleep it off" by himself in a locked room. But as soon as Gizmo is released in the general population, the subluxations return.

2. An old patient of mine, Bishop—a year old at that time, male, mostly Siamese I think, and looked just like Wayne Gretzky—had constant mid-back pain and hated being handled. The little girl of the house, for whom the cat was bought, was depressed because she though Bishop didn't like her. Bishop had no traceable history of injuries, although the breeder mentioned that his own kids were constantly playing with the new kittens. The vet could find nothing wrong, and the family was about to give the cat away to a shelter.

I examined Bishop's spine and found a definite spasm in his lower back (the sixth lumbar). His mid-back also felt tight, but I think the spasm there was a compensation for the lower lumbar subluxation. After a two-minute treatment using the Ligament Push, I flipped Bishop over on his back and did a gentle lumbar roll (both sides). I also found a left atlas subluxation and used a light left atlas release. Two days later, he was a little more approachable but still not cured. I treated him with the same methods four more times over a two-week period. It's been three years now, and Bishop is the most held cat on the block.

3. Strawberry, a three-year-old female Persian, was injured after she accidentally fell out of a two-story window onto soft grass. After the incident, her owner rushed her to the vet, and a set of X-rays were taken which revealed no broken bones. Strawberry was limping due to a front leg sprain, but the owner's main concern was that Strawberry wouldn't eat (she was drinking, though). For three days after the fall, Strawberry just looked at her food and turned away. She went back to the vet for another examination. The vet said that if Strawberry didn't eat within the next three days, she would have to be hospitalized and fed intravenously. Even though cats can live a long time without eating*, this is still a serious concern. So Strawberry was brought to my house in desperation. The owner apologized for barging in on a Sunday, but I was in the mood for a challenge.

I examined Strawberry and felt a definite knot on the left side of her eighth thoracic (mid-back) and a right atlas subluxation. Since Strawberry was so touchy, I decided to adjust each area with the metal mallet (activator), and I also used the Ligament Push. Just in

---

* Dr. David Taylor, D.V.M., wrote about a cat who survived without eating for four weeks. Dr. Taylor cites the following example: "Chips, a marmalade tom from Liverpool, was inadvertently packed into a crate of machine parts and shipped by sea to Mombasa. Four weeks later, when the crate was opened in Africa, Chips was still alive, although he was somewhat thinner. He was thought to have survived by eating some of the grease coating the machinery and lapping up what little moisture developed from condensation."

case the treatment worked, the owner brought her favorite food with her. Within five minutes of the adjustment, Strawberry was eating! She was also guzzling the water. The mid-back subluxation had been irritating her stomach. My favorite cases are the ones where I see immediate results, like this one.

Appendix A

Two Views from Two Vets

A number of progressive and dedicated veterinarians now view chiropractic not only as a powerful health care tool to treat musculoskeletal as well as internal conditions, but often as the treatment of choice. Two of these vets, whom I consider among the best in this country, are Dr. William Inman of Seattle, Washington, and Dr. Hank Kostecki of South Lake Tahoe, California. Both of these practitioners have extensive experience with feline chiropractic and were kind enough to contribute their views and some case studies for this book.

The first viewpoint is by Dr. Inman, who works with me to teach animal chiropractic methods to professionals and laypersons nationwide.

Chiropractic and Cats

Incidence of Feline Diseases Related to Subluxations

Veterinary chiropractic care for the feline exists very much like cats exist in society—that is, detached and seemingly coming from another planet. Certainly all of the disease conditions we see in the canine are present in the feline but with several very important "additions." These "additions" are found to be the major reasons a cat lover would present their pet to a veterinary chiropractor. These syndromes represent some of the easiest and the most difficult conditions to treat in the whole of chiropractic applications in animals.

"Wry-Neck" or Anterior Cervical Disease

The cat that presents with a neck twisted to the side, or more commonly down and to the side, is the "easy fix" that we kitty chiropractors are always hoping to get. These cases usually respond quickly and with few repeat visits. In some cases a single adjustment may be all that is needed to restore complete and permanent function.

The cat that presents with this syndrome—usually due to an acute injury—cannot lift its head up well, or keeps it tucked down and to one side. An injury such as falling off furniture or from a tree, or just rough play with a sibling, can create a subluxation of the first and second cervical vertebrae that will create immediate or delayed symptoms. The owner may complain that the cat woke up one morning with a kink in his neck and hasn't been able to run or jump properly for weeks to months. These cats often present severely compromised.

Jack the cat appeared on my exam table after he had been to three other vets who had not been able to isolate the source of his inability to walk straight, jump up on the couch, or lift his head up to look at his owner. His owner was frustrated and continually complained about the veterinary costs that he had incurred. "If I have to spend one more dime on that damned cat I'm gonna take it out and shoot it in the head!" was his lament, designed to induce me to keep costs to a minimum.

The owner failed to realize that, having just brought his cat to the "kitty chiropractor," his very presence at such an eclectic and unique approach to veterinary health care defined him as a class-A, number-one client, willing to do anything and everything necessary for his beloved pet.

Now this doesn't change the way we work up the case or what it costs. It's just an amusing dance that plays out between vet and client before they both decide to get busy and fix the problem.

Jack could not lift his head up and to the right and could not advance his right leg forward enough to walk naturally. His X-rays showed nothing, which was why he was not treated by the previous veterinarians. He had been this way for two months.

Upon examination and adjustment, Jack's subluxations were the kind for which one adjustment "unlocks" the whole case. One quick and easy motion to the right neck area at the wing of the atlas, directed toward the opposite ear, reduced Jack's atlanto-occipital subluxation for good; all that was left was the rehabilitation phase, which took one week. Jack was jumping up to the top of the refrigerator (his favorite warm spot) without hesitation. Jack's "dad" only had to pay me for an office call and a recheck.

These "hitch in the neck" cases in the feline are the ones that make the veterinary chiropractor look really good and respond very fast. They can be very embarrassing to the referring vets that cannot find the problem on X-ray or examination.

The Skin-Spinal Reflex Phenomenon

The cat has a unique reflex that has been noticed by clients and veterinarians alike. It is an odd reflexive twitching, head-jerking, or licking behavior initiated by stimulation over the lumbo-sacral area of the back. Often this reflex can be triggered by a light touch to the back, as in petting, so it is noticed commonly. The threshold of activation of the reflex can be so close to firing off, due to subluxation irritation, that any stimulation will easily create this response. At times, just holding a hand over the back of the cat and not even touching the skin or hair will trigger the reflex. Veterinarians have marveled at this response for years without understanding it.

This skin-spinal reflex pattern can look like a seizure or a licking spasm directed to the cat's foreleg or shoulder; it is the source of much confusion for practitioners who look for a problem in the front of the pet when the condition lies in spinal nerve root inflammation in the lower back vertebrae.

One of these skin-spinal reflex cases was Ziti, a ten-year-old spayed domestic shorthair presented to my clinic with an unexplained seizure condition. When you touched Ziti on her lower back, she would scream her disapproval and whip around to find something to sink her teeth into. The owner said that she never liked having her back touched and would not allow petting. That was just the way she was.

Ziti also walked with a bit of a limp in her left rear, and she had a chronic dermatitis on her back in the area where the reflex was the most intense. Many of these cases have this associated dermatitis, and it has been thought that the two are different manifestations of the same disease. This skin-spinal syndrome can thus be confused with flea bite allergy and other skin diseases. It is thought that the subluxations associated with the syndrome create a numbness or an irritation sensation in the skin that serves to induce skin disease or create self-trauma by the cat (hence the skin-spinal nomenclature).

Ziti did not like to be touched or adjusted in the area of her lower back, and she was not shy in letting anyone who tried it find that out. My heart goes out to these pets who have had to endure a severe, burning, itching numbness for years. Anyone who approached that area on their backs would do so at their own peril.

X-rays and examination showed the 2nd, 3rd, 4th, and 5th lumbar vertebrae were subluxated and had been that way for many years. Reduction of these subluxations over the next few days would give Ziti immediate relief and obvious reduction of the tell-tale reflex.

Ziti was adjusted weekly for one month. At the end of that time she could be petted by anyone and was even found to be purring for the first time in her life. She could walk and jump without problems, and she appeared on the road to recovery. Ziti's pain and skin condition resolved completely within one year and did not recur.

This condition is one of the few in feline chiropractic care that responds slowly. It can take monthly adjustments for up to a year to get a solution, as opposed to the 5.75 adjustments per case seen in canine cases.

Lumbo-Sacral Subluxation Complex

The classic human and canine subluxation syndrome exists as a problem in the lower back or lumbo-sacral region. Cats also have similar injuries and clinical signs associated with these subluxations. Most often, reluctance to jump up onto bed or couch, or to climb stairs, is seen as a clinical indicator.

Cats are usually much easier to adjust than people or dogs. These subluxations often resolve within two or three adjustments and seldom return. It is my belief that cats are easier to adjust than dogs because their bones are straighter, their vertebrae are easier to position, and they have longer bodies relative to their width. Also, their joints are more mobile, and chiropractic contact points are easier to find.

Buster, a five-year-old neutered male Burmese, would crouch at the base of the sofa, preparing to spring into the loving laps of his owners—then pause as if to contemplate a potential shooting pain that would ensue if he did so. Buster would then slink off to lie on a favored spot on the floor.

Lack of rear leg strength is often the owner's complaint, indicating a lumbo-sacral subluxation. In these cases, X-rays are often unremarkable, and other diagnostic means give no clues save a diagnostic chiropractic evaluation. Such a diagnostic evaluation will reveal that subluxations exist between T-10 (the tenth thoracic vertebra) and L-7 (the seventh lumbar), that is, in the lower part of the spine.

Within the 3 to 5 adjustments that are needed to solve the problem, the clinical signs fall away in the first two weeks. These cases are usually quickly reduced and solved, however, they may recur again during the cat's life.

Buster presented these symptoms again twice within the next five years, and it was my contention that the owners discontinued scheduled adjustments before his cycle of healing was completed. While Buster was clinically fine, he was not completely healed.

The most important adjustment is the last adjustment, at which the patient is found to need no further adjustment.

The Caudal Cervical Syndrome

Towards the back or bottom of the neck area (caudal cervicals), the neck is forced to absorb all the stress of the body's motion relative to the mass of the head. This places an inordinate amount of strain on the vertebrae in the area of the 5th, 6th, and 7th cervical vertebrae. Over time, even the relatively small mass of the cat's head will predispose the joints of the neck to subluxations. Rough play with litter mates or siblings is also considered contributory.

Bitsy, a five-year-old, 18-pound spayed female domestic shorthair who waddled when she tried to walk, was anything but "bitsy." Bitsy presented with a very unique gait, to say the least. She was today, not waddling, but walking on her shoulders and chin. That's right, she was pushing herself around with her rear legs only, and her front legs were held out straight, dragging behind her. It would almost have been comical if it were not so sad. She was happy, seemed to be adjusting well to her sudden infirmity (which occurred almost overnight), and illustrated no external signs of trauma. Yet Bitsy was in trouble.

For this syndrome to occur, there could be no doubt as to

where the problem was located. Spastic paralysis of the front legs which left the rear legs untouched had to mean a lesion in the caudal cervical area, on the dorsum or top of the spinal cord. (This condition in the canine almost always causes the rear legs to become involved also and the whole animal is down, not just the front.) It could have been a tumor that was compromising the spinal cord at that point, but since it occurred overnight, I hoped it was a subluxation that could be treated.

I asked the owner how long Bitsy had been walking around like a wheelbarrow, and she told me it had been over a week. Perhaps she thought the condition would go away at any moment.

Bitsy seemed resigned to her "new slant on life," but I realized this would soon take this cat's life.

Bitsy's subluxations were treated, and the next day she was able to stand and walk. Three weeks later, Bitsy was her old self again, to be found waddling around the house on a direct line from her food dish to her favorite perch, surveying her front yard from the comfort of her warm house. What a life!

Veterinary Orthopedic Manipulation (V.O.M.™)

The technique I employ in adjusting cats is one I've developed and used on all domestic animals since 1983. In over 45,000 adjustments, I have yet to injure an animal, and the number of lives saved with this technique is truly the one major accomplishment I have made in my life.

Using a hand-held device called an Activator™ (an instrument developed by Arlan Fuhr, D.C., and generically known as the metal mallet), or Activator Methods, I can quickly and easily reduce virtually any subluxation in domestic animals, particularly cats. The Activator uses a small mass coupled with an incredibly fast pulse of motion of the mass to effect an adjustment. The small mass of the instrument cannot cause a torsional or mechanical stress of muscles, nerves, or other soft tissue. It is totally safe!

Manual adjustment techniques are more adaptable to the feline than the other domestic animals (save the horse) because of the relative ease of mobility of the joints of the cat. Certainly a peaceful and tractable feline patient can be positioned and manipulated easily, relative to a 150-pound Irish Wolfhound who is in severe pain and is anxious as to what you are doing to the area of their body that is in acute pain. A cat with the same concern is in a similarly poor mood, but with the Activator device, the adjustment occurs before the pet has time to think about what is going to happen.

A painful or apprehensive kitty can at times be found as a solid mass of resistant muscle and thus impossible to adjust, yet the Activator can easily move these subluxations to reduction, even if the patient resists with all its might.

Due to its speed, efficacy, safety, and unlimited application, instrument adjusting is the fastest-growing modality of feline chiropractic adjustment in the U.S. and is the one that I teach in a national seminar series (*Veterinary Chiropractic: Small Animal Module One*). For more information, please contact me (William L. Inman, D.V.M.) at 206-523-9917 (voice), 206-522-7512 (fax), or Drbill42@aol.com (e-mail).

This next viewpoint was written by Dr. Henry Kostecki, who is not only a holistic veterinarian but a avid supporter of animal chiropractic.

SOME EXPERIENCES WITH CHIROPRACTIC FOR ANIMALS

Had I not personally tried out chiropractic manipulation upon animals with my own two hands, I might have remained a skeptic—as ignorant of the multitudinous benefits of the art as the next person with a closed mind. After all, when a certain form of therapy just isn't working so well for you, why not have a look around to see what else might be out there to benefit one's patients without causing any harm? About the worst I've ever seen in terms of any undesirable effects from adjusting an animal is that the maneuver just plain *didn't work*; not that my patient stopped eating or perhaps started vomiting the very medication that was intended to alleviate pain and discomfort. An old veterinarian back in the early '70s once told me, "They just don't need all those drugs you learned about in school—in fact, I end up giving most of 'em just vitamins and watch them just get better on their own."

This was a new realization for me twenty-five years or so ago when I first began to practice veterinary medicine. However, it was a well-established realization for my experienced colleague. Both our intuitions were telling us that something was not necessarily wrong with the medicine we had been instructed in—just that our knowledge of therapeutics was clearly limited to only that which was taught to us. I wanted to know what else I could be doing as an adjunct to, or perhaps as a replacement for, the standard treatments. This seemed especially important for chronic conditions where the torment was often unrelenting and the prospect for improvement without side effects from standard therapies was remote. We needed safe, effective alternatives to what we were already doing. However, back then, therapies like acupuncture, homeopathy, herbology, and most certainly chiropractic care—treatments which actually can get to the heart of the problem—were just so many alien words to us (if these things were any good, why weren't they taught in school?) until personal investigation with an open mind began!

After many years of practice, it has become abundantly clear to me that almost anything can and does go wrong almost anywhere in the body, given enough time. Thus, it should be no surprise the particularly complex central nervous system (brain and spinal cord), housed in a flexible, multi-jointed vertebral column and skull, composed of so many relatively small bones, should be subject to a simple-to-understand and commonly occurring pathology known as subluxations (which are dislocations without the dramatic displacement of components with which we are likely familiar).

The pain and dysfunction resulting to an area from nerve compression is clearly best treated by manipulation of the affected area back to its normal configuration. This is what chiropractic is all about. It is not about the strength or force the practitioner applies; rather, it is all about precision usage of small forces. In fact, with around 150 or so complete systems of chiropractic available to the practitioner, it should be noted here that some methods (i.e., network, directional non-force, and cranio-sacral chiropractic, to name just a few) use not much more than finger-pressure force. And yes, small forces are perfectly adequate to adjust big horses in many instances.

Not long ago, I was asked to look at an eight-week-old kitten who, after running full speed into a table leg a couple weeks back, had been walking sort of sideways like a crab every since. Nothing seemed to hurt the kitten when I touched its neck, but I felt a distinct deviation of those tiny bones to one side. After announcing to its caregiver my intention to adjust the baby's neck, and noting her open-mouthed stare in response (I suppose she wasn't expecting an adjustment), I quickly proceeded to perform a "rotary break" move on its little neck before said person could muster a "no." The "move" resulted in popping and crunching noises which could be heard down the hall. The kitten proceeded to yawn and stretch, then walk off henceforth straight as a bullet—I suppose to find another table leg—while the caregiver, visibly shaken by the "audibles," was assisted out of the room by her friend.

Another example of the usefulness of chiropractic was when I adjusted the lower back of a dachshund who hadn't wagged her tail for years. After treatment, the owner was astounded, most of all by the tail wagging, "just like when she was a puppy—and I thought she was getting old, Doc."

Then there was the case of another little dachshund who just couldn't get into a comfortable position to go to sleep— you know, endless circling. A rib was out of place, and one little pull was all I needed to do. Even though that caregiver has around a dozen or so of the breed, all of whom I've adjusted at one time or another, he's still talking about that rib and what a difference it made to the old girl.

And then a case of a cat who urinated without much awareness of the event became my responsibility one day. She had been to the appropriate specialists and was treated by them without benefit. They said it was a spinal problem—and they were right, the cat having suffered a fall. One adjustment was all it took to restore function, and I thought we were sure lucky with her.

A very common presentation is the old dog who can't get up so well anymore and, once up, doesn't go very far due to pain. These old-timers are always a challenge for any therapeutic method, and their treatment usually involves an adjustment, nutritional counseling as well as "nutraceuticals," and other complimentary treatments.

I've witnessed chronic sinusitis clear up with neck adjustments, temperament changes for the better, hearing improvements, chronic foot chewing go away (which was likely related to shooting nerve pain or tingling sensations), even some skin conditions improve, all with chiropractic.

Animals get traumatized, often endure chronic toxicity and emotional stress—all of which contribute to subluxations. Now I know what to do about it.

Appendix B

EXTRA! EXTRA!
(Animal Chiropractic in the Press)

Here are a few newspaper and magazine articles that were either sent to me or are *about* me. **Note:** The only articles I've included about myself concern animal chiropractic (there have been others, but that's for a different book altogether).

The first two articles (letters to the editor, B.J. Palmer) were published on August 12, 1921 in *The Fountainhead News*, the official newspaper of the Palmer School of Chiropractic in Davenport, Iowa. Palmer was the first chiropractic school, founded in 1895.

* * *

MORE INFO ON ADJUSTING
OTHER ANIMALS THAN HUMANS
By Clay L. Dean, D.C., & C.D. Kinney, D.C.

Dear B.J.: I notice the article in the August 6th FN [Fountainhead News] of "Chiropractic for Mules." Well, here is one

"Chiropractic for Mules." During the "flu" epidemic of 1918 and 1919 I was adjusting Henry Vinson's son for an incoordination causing pneumonia. It was dark and raining and quite cold. Mr. Vinson says, "Doc, I have a mule that is down in the back and can't get up and wish you would come out and see if you can do something for him." The mule was up on his front feet endeavoring to get up, but had little or no use of his hind legs. I adjusted the mule between the hip bones and said to Vinson, "That may help the mule." When I went to see the son the next day, Vinson reported to me that when he went out the next morning the mule was standing up at the stack eating hay and he reported to me later that the mule was at work, and apparently all right.

About two years ago I was called to attend Mr. Ben Vandalsem's Scotch Collie who was dragging his hind legs, and after adjusting the dog he improved and got quite normal and is a fine active dog today. I am confident that Chiropractic will apply in all vertebrates. I am—

Yours Chiropractically,
Clay L. Dean, D.C.

Dear B.J.: Here is a brutal case: Cow down, all swelled up, as if she would burst. Owner with horse saddled ready to start for Veterinarian, called me in as I was passing by to ask what I knew about sick cows. Cow was in barn night before, gorged herself, action of stomach ceased. A poisoned condition set in. I adjust sixth and eighth dorsals and K.P. (Kidney Place). In two minutes cow was up vomiting. I came back by in one hour, cow seemingly in normal condition. Veterinarian hearing of me depriving him of a fee asked, "What right I had to practice?" "The right of any freeborn American."

Regret I cannot be with you all at Homecoming.

Very truly,
C.D. Kinney.

* * *

This next article was first published on October 29, 1996 by syndicated columnist Mike Royko of the *Chicago Tribune*. It has since been reprinted by several chiropractic publications as well as newspapers around the country. (This got my phone ringing!)

ANIMAL CHIROPRACTOR HAS A BONE TO PICK WITH STATE AGENCY

Because my dog likes to chase his tail, I suspect that he has a spine that is out of whack.

It stands to reason. As an experiment, just get down on all fours, pretend you have a tail and try to chase it. Not just once but a dozen times.

If you do this often enough, you will wind up with a back that has cricks, creaks, aches and pains.

But as a human being, you have resources to cure your aching back—possibly a chiropractor.

In my tail-chasing dog's case, such treatment is not available. So some day, I could have a mutt that walks sideways, limps, or moans from back pains.

That is because we have a strange law in this state that makes it illegal for a chiropractor to treat animals.

I discovered this in talking to Dr. Daniel Kamen of Buffalo Grove, a chiropractor who is expert in treating animal ailments.

He is one of the few chiropractors who can claim to have adjusted the spines of a giraffe, lions, ferrets, cows, rabbits, dogs and cats.

The giraffe was his toughest challenge since he had to climb an 11-foot ladder to do the job; the giraffe was unpleasant, and as a result, he later had to have his own spine adjusted.

"I've done rabbits. I had a patient who had a rabbit that was really lame. A veterinarian gave it medication and wanted to do surgery. But the owner brought it to me, and it had only one vertebra that needed adjustment. I did it and it was a perky bunny again.

"Horses are easy because most are already trained. Horses, especially racehorses, get athletic injuries. They also throw their lower back out often because people get on them on the left side and it drags the left side of their back down. They have neck problems from people tugging the reins."

"For dogs, it's the choke collar that does it. Our necks are the same as a dog's. Imagine if someone had a chain around your neck and they yanked it 30 times a day. You'd take them to court. Dogs can't tell a person to cut it out."

For all his expertise on animal ailments, you won't find even a gerbil in Kamen's waiting room.

"My main practice is with people. But I teach a nationwide seminar to chiropractors, veterinarians and laymen on the adjusting techniques.

"But the veterinarians don't like that. So the Illinois Department of Professional Regulation visited my office, and they were upset that I treated animals and they warned me against it.

"I said, 'Look, if you give me trouble, I'll write a book and get it published so everyone can know how to do this.'

"So the veterinarians are screaming. More recently, an investigator came to my office looking for animals. I never bring animals to my human office. But they told me that if I continue practicing on animals, I would get a fine or have my license suspended. So now I just teach seminars. And I'm forced to demonstrate on a stuffed dog. I don't do the seminars in Illinois. I've had them in 20 other states.

"It's sad that the average person can get a hunting license and shoot a deer's head off, but I can't adjust an animal's spine.

"I've been a chiropractor for 15 years. I started working with animals when I was in college. I happened to hear a yelp coming out of a professor's office and I went in and he was doing a dog.

"So he took me out to a farm and we adjusted the cows. Cows are tough to adjust because they stand in the stalls so much and don't move around and their spines get really stiff.

"Because of this stupid law, I told the inspectors that they left me no choice but to write a book so people could learn to adjust their own animals.

"So I did. The book came out a few weeks ago, and it's

called *The Well-Adjusted Dog: Canine Chiropractic Methods You Can Do*. But you can use the methods on any mammal."

Tony Sanders, a spokesman for the Illinois Department of Professional Regulation, explained the conflict:

"It is out of the scope of a physician's practice to treat animals. Veterinarians are the only ones who can treat or manipulate animals. We have one case from 1993 that ended up with a chiropractor being indefinitely suspended for practicing on animals. Physicians, surgeons and chiropractors can only treat human ailments; veterinarians can only treat animals. That's the way the law is written in Illinois."

So if my tail-chasing mutt ends up being permanently shaped like a doughnut, I'll know who to blame.

Is there anything politicians don't goof up?

Appendix C

Where to Find Animal Chiropractors

It's actually getting easier to find a professional person in your area who is proficient in animal chiropractic techniques. Through various teaching programs, such as the seminars I conduct along with Dr. Bill Inman, more chiropractors and veterinarians are including animal chiropractic as part of their regular services.

If your veterinarian or chiropractor does not perform this service, or can't due to legal restrictions, then you may call my office at 1-800-742-8433. I have amassed a list of over 1,500 doctors nationwide who have some expertise in animal adjusting, including horses.

For those chiropractors who wish to practice with a vet but don't know which ones would be amicable to this business arrangement, then contact a vet who is a member of one the holistic organizations listed below. They tend to be more sympathetic towards chiropractic.

1. American Holistic Veterinary Medical Association
   2214 Old Emmorton Rd.
   Bel Air, MD 21015
   (410) 569-0795

2. International Veterinary Acupuncture Society (IVAS)
   c/o Meredith L. Snader, V.M.D.
   2140 Conestoga Road
   Chester Springs, PA 19425
   (303) 258-3767

3. Toxicology Hotline for Animals
   University of Illinois College of Veterinary Medicine
   2001 S. Lincoln Ave.
   Urbana, IL 61801
   1-800-548-2423

4. California Holistic Veterinary Medical Association
   c/o Beth Wildermann, D.V.M.
   17333 Bear Creek Rd.
   Boulder Creek, CA 95006

5. Dr. Bill Inman, D.V.M.
   7769 58th N.E.
   Seattle, WA 98115
   (206) 523-9917

6. Dr. Daniel Kamen
   Kamen Chiropractic
   3421 N. Arlington Hts. Rd.
   Arlington Heights, IL 60004
   (847) 394-3530
   1-800-742-8433

BIBLIOGRAPHY

1. Gatterman, Meridel I. *Chiropractic Management of Spine-Related Disorders*. Williams & Wilkins, 1990.
2. Gerstenfeld, Sheldon L. *The Cat Care Book*. Addison-Wesley Publishing Company, Inc., 1989.
3. Getty, Robert. *The Anatomy of the Domestic Animals*. W.B. Saunders Company, 1975.
4. Kamen, Daniel. *The Well Adjusted Dog*. Brookline Books, 1996.
5. Medford, Myles A. "Veterinary Chiropractic: Feasible, Practical and Proves Chiropractic Premise"; *Digest of Chiropractic Economics*, November/December 1980 (Part I) and January/February 1981 (Part II).
6. Miller, Malcolm E. *Anatomy of the Dog*. W.B. Saunders Company, 1964.
7. Oliver, John E., & Lorenz, Michael D. *Handbook of Veterinary Neurology*. W.B. Saunders Company, 1993.
8. Stein, Diane. *Natural Healing for Dogs & Cats*. The Crossing Press, 1993.
9. Stein, Diane. *The Natural Remedy Book for Dogs & Cats*. The Crossing Press, 1994.
10. Siegal, Mordecai. *The Cornell Book of Cats*. Villard Books, 1992.
11. Stephenson, R.W. *Chiropractic Text Book*. Palmer School of Chiropractic, 1927.
12. Taylor, David. *You & Your Cat*. Alfred Knopf, 1986.

MARKETPLACE

1. **Videos** on animal adjusting (cats, dogs, and horses). Each 60-minute VHS video demonstrates easy-to-do animal chiropractic methods. Anatomy as well as adjusting techniques are covered. $29.95 each; 2 for $49.95; all three for $69.95. Illinois residents include 8¼% sales tax.

2. **Metal mallet (activator*).** $149.00. Illinois residents add 8¼% sales tax ($12.29).

3. **Book—*The Well Adjusted Dog: Canine Chiropractic Methods You Can Do.*** $16.95. The first book on animal chiropractic; available in most bookstores or from Brookline Books, 1-800-666-2665. Signed copies may be ordered from Dr. Kamen at the address below.

Add $3.50 S&H to your total order.
Send check payable to:
Kamen Chiropractic
3421 N. Arlington Hts. Rd.
Arlington Heights, IL 60004
or call 1-800-742-8433

---

* Activator™ is a trademark of Activator Methods Inc., Phoenix, AZ. The metal mallet sold here is manufactured by Moyco Union Broach.

INDEX

About the Author

Dr. Daniel Kamen was born on June 18th, 1956, in Chicago, Illinois. He has been practicing chiropractic since 1981. His father is a highly respected anesthesiologist; his mother, a gifted artist. Dr. Kamen's original animal chiropractic organization, "Animal Crackers," produced animal chiropractic educational materials, which taught others how to adjust dogs and horses.

Dr. Kamen lives with his wife, Sharon, of eighteen years, along with their three sons, Jeffrey, Gary and Kevin. He makes his home in Buffalo Grove, Illinois. Dr. Kamen has been featured on many TV, radio, and newspaper stories concerning his work with animal chiropractic. He currently is on tour, teaching a professional as well as a lay lecture seminar on animal chiropractic (horse and dog adjusting). His hobbies include playing the piano and chess (master level).

FREE OFFER!

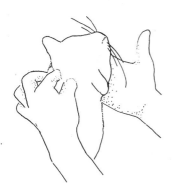

Return the form below to receive a FREE national directory of practitioners of animal chiropractic, plus a coupon for ONE FREE ADJUSTMENT for your pet! Mail to:

Attn: Directory Offer
Brookline Books
P.O. Box 1047
Cambridge, MA 02238-1047

Dear Brookline Books,

I am interested in professional chiropractic care for my cat. Please send me a FREE national directory of chiropractors and veterinarians who offer this service, along with a coupon for ONE FREE ADJUSTMENT from a participating practitioner.

Name _____

Address _____

_____

City _____

State _____ ZIP _____ — _____
